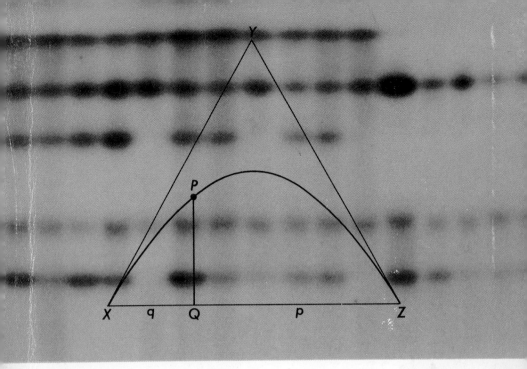

CURRENT CONCEPTS IN BIOLOGY SERIES

Process and Pattern in Evolution

Terrell H. Hamilton

Foreword by Ernst Mayr

Process and Pattern in Evolution

Cover photo is of a starch gel showing electrophoretic variation in esterase isozymes of single individuals of *Drosophila nasuta* from Malaya and various islands of the Pacific. (Photo courtesy of F. M. Johnson and Carmen G. Kanapi, The University of Texas.) Imposed upon the photo is a drawing of homogeneous coordinates fixing the proportions of homozygotes and heterozygotes on a parabola (P) for a pair of alleles in an equilibrium population under random mating.

CURRENT CONCEPTS IN BIOLOGY
A Macmillan Series
NORMAN H. GILES, WALTER KENWORTHY, JOHN G. TORREY, Editors

Process and Pattern in Evolution

Terrell H. Hamilton
The University of Texas

The Macmillan Company, New York
Collier-Macmillan Limited, London

Library of Congress catalog card number: 67–18123

The Macmillan Company, New York

Collier-Macmillan Canada, Ltd., Toronto, Ontario

Printed in the United States of America

Foreword

EVOLUTIONARY BIOLOGY, founded by Darwin in 1859, has greatly matured in the more than one hundred years since then. It is no longer necessary to enumerate painstakingly the proofs for evolution; with evolution accepted by every scientist, the emphasis has shifted. The words *Process and Pattern* in the title of this book describe clearly the current interest. What are the moving forces of evolution? What are the various mechanisms and their interactions? What are the resulting patterns of organic diversity?

Terrell H. Hamilton in a novel approach attempts, very successfully, to answer such questions. Starting from the simplest premises he tries to bring the reader right to the current frontiers of evolutionary research. I say *frontiers* because evolutionary biology is moving at present on many different fronts, and exciting new findings are being made on all of them.

Species diversity on islands and mainlands, in temperate and tropical areas, is one of the frontiers—to which Hamilton himself has made significant original contributions. The application of the findings of population genetics to population ecology is another. Quite rightly, natural selection is the center of attention throughout this volume. It is in this emphasis that the current generation of evolutionists feels so close to the Darwin of 1859. Like him, we are awed by the universality of differential reproduction, which results in the uneven representation of different genes and gene-combinations in the next generation. For evolution is nothing less than such systematic genetic changes, correlated with certain factors in the environment.

And yet it is not the gene that is the unit of selection, but rather the whole individual. It is the "goodness" of the whole organism that natural selection evaluates and either rewards or discriminates against.

The interaction of the genes in the genotype and the translation of the genotype into the phenotype are thus also the concern of the evolutionist. Finally, it is the performance of the individual in his environment that decides upon his fitness, because it is the environment which exerts the selection pressure. Therefore, ecology and evolutionary biology overlap broadly.

It is now evident why there has been such a vigorous revival of evolutionary biology in recent decades. Whether we are active in the fields of ecology, behavior, or molecular biology, questions of fitness, of adaptation, and of the historical nature of the genetic program are asked everywhere. But there is an all too apparent danger that the wrong questions will be asked, or the wrong answers be given, unless we truly understand the nature of the evolutionary processes. Hamilton's perceptively written volume is a welcome contribution to this understanding.

ERNST MAYR

Preface

THIS BOOK was written as an introduction to natural selection and the adaptations that differentiate and characterize animal species. The emphasis of the text is on principles of evolution. Students start with a historical account of the Darwin-Wallace concept of evolution by natural selection, proceed to a moderately detailed account of population genetics and ecology, and conclude with an examination of various trends in speciation and evolution. The examples illustrating the latter topic—that of patterns in speciation and evolution—are taken mostly from recent work by evolutionists concerned with contemporary animal species. The book ends with my own interpretation and terminology for evolution theory. This interpretation emphasizes the reproducing individual as the unit of selection, the gene or gene substitution as the unit or unit process of population adaptation, and the species as the unit of evolution.

Two points of clarification may be necessary. First, a clear-cut distinction is made between adaptation and evolution. Adaptation is the adjustment of populations to their environment by the operation of natural selection. Evolution is considered to be the observable result of adaptation at different points in time and space. In this sense, natural selection results in adaptation, and adaptation results in evolution. Second, and this point relates to the first, there are two kinds of variations discernable in nature, both of which are all-important in adaptation and evolution. This important idea has recently been clarified by Ernst Mayr in his *Animal Species and Evolution. Individual variations* are those occurring within populations. This is the topic of intrapopulational variation. *Group variations* are seen when we compare differences or mean values for measurements of characteristics of different populations, races, or species. This is the topic of interpopulational variation.

In brief, individual variations within populations are the substrate of natural selection, whereas group variations are the results of adaptation. Differences among the latter, in turn, reflect evolutionary change.

The mathematics of evolution theory has been kept to a minimum and what there is can be bypassed. It is presented for the student who wants to go a little further in visualizing mathematically the theory of natural selection and equilibrium phenomena for diversity of organic life. The terminology used in this book assumes a knowledge of high school zoology and botany, including some genetics, and an awareness of the principles of taxonomy and classification.

Several times in the text I have discussed only briefly certain topics in adaptation or ecology which for full comprehension demand more advanced training in biology, mathematics, and statistics than the beginning student has usually experienced. In these instances I have not hesitated to refer the student to other texts or to the original sources. There can be no doubt that the first-year undergraduate now has a better secondary education than we previously assumed, and that he is capable of more independent work than we usually demand.

In writing this book, I am especially indebted to Ernst Mayr, Robert K. Selander, Robert H. Barth, Jr., Ira Rubinoff, and Guy L. Bush. In various ways they have helped with the preparation of the manuscript as well as contributing to my own thinking about evolution. The line drawings were made by Peter Loewer, whose assistance is appreciated. Finally, I am indebted to my colleagues in the Department of Zoology at The University of Texas and to Sir Peter Medawar at the National Institute for Medical Research in London for providing both an academic atmosphere and an excellent facility for the writing of this book.

T. H. H.

Contents

The Darwin-Wallace Concept of Evolution by Natural Selection

As many more individuals of each species are born than can possibly survive; and as, consequently, there is a frequently recurring struggle for existence, it follows that any being, if it varies however slightly in any manner profitable to itself, under the complex and sometimes varying conditions of life, will have a better chance of surviving, and thus be naturally selected. *From the strong principle of inheritance, any selected variety will tend to propagate its new and modified form.*

DARWIN, 1859, p. 5.

THIS IS ONE WAY that Charles Robert Darwin (1809–1882) stated his theory of evolution by natural selection. His book was entitled *On the Origin of Species by Means of Natural Selection, or the Preservation of Favoured Races in the Struggle for Life,* and the word *evolution* does not occur in it. The book appeared in 1859, shortly after a joint reading at the Linnean Society of London in 1858 of papers prepared on the topic by both Darwin and Alfred Russell Wallace (1823–1913). Wallace, during his travels in the East Indies, formulated a theory of natural selection that was essentially the same as Darwin's. Wallace recorded later that the idea of survival of the fittest came to him during a period of illness in the Moluccas in February, 1858. The theory was finally thought out during a fever, written in several evenings, and sent to Darwin by the next mail. Darwin received the manuscript on June 18 and immediately recognized his own theory. In a letter he wrote the geologist Lyell that very day, he states: "I never saw a more striking co-incidence." Lyell and the botanist Hooker arranged the joint reading of Wallace's essay and one by Darwin. While we should perhaps speak of the Darwin-Wallace concept of natural selection, major recognition is usually given to Darwin. Wallace himself gave such recognition to Darwin. Considering Darwin's early attainment of the concept (1835–1837), his success with the "Origin" book, and his phenomenal scientific productivity in fields of scientific investigation other than evolution, the universal recognition given him seems not unwarranted.

Of historical interest is the fact that Darwin's book was published in London with a first edition of 1,250 copies, nearly all of which were bought on the first day of issue (November 24, 1859). There is good evidence that the Darwin-Wallace concept of evolution by natural selection had already permeated the scientific community before Darwin's book was published. The papers by the two evolutionists read before the Linnean Society on July 1, 1858, had been published jointly on August 20, in the Society's journal. And in October, 1859, a month before publication of the "Origin," the first acknowledged application of the new theory appeared. H. B. Tristram used it to explain the particular colors of birds adapted to desert and other environmental conditions. That this first application of their concept (appearing in *The Ibis,* journal of the British Ornithologists' Union) deals with adaptation in birds is indicative of a lead that ornithology took, and until recently continued to take, in the task of elucidating evolutionary processes.

In general, remarkable parallels exist for the respective experiences of Darwin and Wallace prior to reaching a comparable conclusion. For example, both traveled extensively in the tropical latitudes: Darwin in South America and the Galápagos Archipelago; Wallace in the Amazon basin and the East Indies. Each read and ultimately reacted to the "Essay on Population" by Malthus, which contained, along with the idea of geometric increase in population in a limiting environment, the expression *struggle for existence.* We may guess that each coupled in his mind two observations or sets of information: (1) an awareness of the past and present distributions and morphological characteristics of plants and animals suggesting nonrandom or orderly trends correlated with attributes of the environment; (2) an understanding of the array of individual variations from which the "environment selects" those better fitted for contributions of offspring to the next generation. So to speak, they placed differential reproduction and survival on a Malthusian background of organisms producing more offspring than can survive, and then developed the concept of evolution by natural selection.

It is of value here to summarize the Darwin-Wallace concept of how evolution occurs by natural selection:

1. Organisms produce far more offspring than can ever survive to become reproducing individuals.

2. Because the numbers of individuals in species are for the most part constant, there must be a high death rate.
3. Individuals are not identical, but vary in their characteristics.
4. Those variants that naturally fit their environments will be favored over those less fit. By inheritance those individuals better fit will pass their characteristics on to the next and future generations in greater numbers than those less fit.
5. The following generations of individuals will exhibit, and continue to improve, the adaptations realized in gradual changes by their ancestors.

Although this listing of steps in evolution by natural selection approximately summarizes the statements of both Darwin and Wallace, their respective theories—as presented in 1858, and again in 1859 by Darwin—differ in points of emphasis. Darwin emphasized clearly, following Malthus, that while individuals and populations have a remarkable potential for increase in numbers, in reality they remain on the average fairly constant in numbers. He thus concluded that natural populations are kept in check "by recurrent struggles against other species or against external nature." At this point, Darwin developed his idea of survival of the fittest in the following manner: "Yearly more are bred than can survive; the smallest gain in balance, in the long run, must tell on which death must fall, and which shall survive. Let this work of selection on one hand, and death on the other, go on for a thousand generations. Who will pretend to affirm that it would produce no effect, when we remember what, in a few years [artificial selection effected in cattle and sheep] by this identical principle of selection."

In such ways Darwin concluded that advantageous, heritable variations—however small—are preserved and in turn accumulate in species. He reasoned that with time and change in local environment, or with dispersal and encounter of new environments, species depart increasingly from their ancestral or parental form. Today we refer to such changes as *phyletic evolution*. Darwin distinguished no qualitative difference between artificial selection and natural selection. In contemporary terms, one can say that he used knowledge of results of artificial selection by man to explain evolution by natural selection.

Wallace also emphasized that although species have tremendous potential for increase in numbers, they still maintain constant or near-constant population sizes. He concluded that most natural populations have their potential for increase in numbers checked by food shortages and other limiting factors. From this, he inferred that the abundance or rareness of a species results from the capacities of its members to combat their limiting factors. Like Darwin, he believed that the external condition, or the environment, is usually limiting or harsh, and that this results in a situation wherein individuals or species compete for food, space, special habitats, mates, or other factors in limited supply.

We must disregard here the many other contributions to biology and evolution made by these two investigators. Among these are Darwin's theory of sexual selection and Wallace's studies in zoogeography. Darwin in particular was ahead of his time in his far-reaching thought, and many of his scientific predictions were to be realized only in our century. The following two instances illustrate this point.

Major Leonard Darwin in conversation with E. B. Ford noted that his father once said that by choosing the right material it might be possible to detect evolutionary changes in natural populations within a period of fifty years. Ford in his own studies, and in summarizing those of others (for example, H. B. D. Kettlewell's investigation of industrial melanism), has superbly documented this prediction by Darwin. Such examples are discussed in Chapter 4, along with the research of R. K. Selander and R. F. Johnston, demonstrating rapid ecogeographic adaptation in the house sparrow introduced into North America during the last century.

In another instance, quoted (p. 271) by Sir Gavin de Beer in 1956, Darwin wrote "It is often said that all the conditions for the first production of a living organism are now present, which could ever have been present. But if (and oh! what a big if!) we could conceive in some warm little pond, with all sorts of ammonia, and phosphoric salts, light, heat, electricity, *etc.*, present, that a proteine compound was chemically formed ready to undergo still more complex changes, at the present day such matter would be instantly devoured or absorbed, which would not have been the case before living creatures were formed." Thus in 1871 Darwin anticipated by some eighty years the possibility of a chemical evolution of proteins. In 1951, S. L. Miller demonstrated that an electrical discharge in a nonliving environment of hydrogen, water, ammonia, and methane resulted in the production of various organic compounds, including acetic acid, formic acid, and most of the amino acids.

Darwin's and Wallace's concept of evolution by natural selection was not without errors or weaknesses. In most instances this was unavoidable, a result of lack of knowledge of biological systems at the time of their study. To cite a specific case, in 1858 and 1859 chromosomes and genes were completely unknown. Darwin and Wallace knew that some variations were inherited simply from observing the passage of traits of parents to their offspring. But they had no convincing mechanism to explain how such heritable characters were passed. Darwin at various times followed Lamarckian theory and presented concepts of pangenesis (where gemmules are thought to be given off by all parts of the body and transported by the blood stream to the germ cells) and blending inheritance. At that time the particulate inheritance of Mendelian genetics was yet to come (see Chapter 2). Still another criticism of Darwin's book is that, despite the "Origin" title, it had little to do with the mechanism of origin of new species from parental species. The role of geographic isolation, like the role of mutation and recombination in particulate genetic variation, was to become widely understood only in the present century.

It would be difficult to summarize the achievements of Darwin and Wallace, or the impact of their work on late nineteenth- and twentieth-century science. For the purposes of this introductory book, however, it should be noted that both men considered adaptation to environment to represent evolution by natural selection of the individual. In other words, they considered the individual to be the unit of natural selection. Their theory of natural selection assumed unequivocally that species are mutable; thus they challenged, among other ideas, the belief that species were instantaneously created. Although a few before them had taken the view that species were subject to change, Darwin and Wallace were more successful in formulation of theory and accumulation of evidence. In ways sufficiently clear and complete to attract others to their position, they altered a generation's way of thinking. Contemporary science is indebted to Darwin and Wallace for the principle of mutability of species. Concepts of natural selection and evolution follow from the idea of gradual accumulation of small, but favorable changes. Students believing or interested in the premise that the history of science and of great ideas is the history of great men can do no better than to study the many writings of these two evolutionists. The effects of Darwin's book transcended biology and entered the realms of philosophy, sociology, and political theory. Karl Marx wanted to dedicate a part of *Das Kapital* to Darwin, but Darwin declined the honor.

Further Reading

Barzun, J. *Darwin, Marx, Wagner*. Boston: Little, Brown, and Company, 1941.

Bell, P. R. *Darwin's Biological Work*. London: Cambridge University Press, 1959.

Carter, G. S. *A Hundred Years of Evolution*. New York: The Macmillan Company, 1957.

Darwin, C. *The Autobiography of Charles Darwin* (*1877*). Edited with restoration of original omissions, notes, and an appendix by Nora Barlow. New York: Harcourt, Brace and Company, 1959.

———. *The Life and Letters of Charles Darwin*. Two volumes and an autobiographical chapter edited by Francis Darwin. New York: D. Appleton and Company, 1897.

————. *On the Origin of Species by Means of Natural Selection* (*1859*). Facsimile of the first edition with an introduction by E. Mayr. Cambridge, Mass.: Harvard University Press, 1964.

————, and A. R. Wallace. *Evolution by Natural Selection*. Papers by C. Darwin and A. R. Wallace edited with a foreword by Sir Gavin de Beer. London: Cambridge University Press, 1958.

de Beer, Sir Gavin. *Charles Darwin, A Scientific Biography*. Garden City, New York: Doubleday and Company, Inc. (Anchor Books), 1965.

Ford, E. B. *Ecological Genetics*. New York: John Wiley and Sons, Inc., 1964.

Huxley, J. and H. B. D. Kettlewell. *Charles Darwin and His World*. London: Thames and Hudson, 1965.

Malthus, T. B. *First Essay on Population* (*1798*). Reprinted. London: Macmillan and Company, 1926.

Wallace, A. R. *Darwinism*. London: Macmillan and Company, 1889.

————. *Natural Selection and Tropical Nature*. London: Macmillan and Company, 1870.

The Nature and Sources of Individual Genetic Variations

Any variation which is not inherited is unimportant for us.

DARWIN, 1859, p. 12.

THE CONTINUOUS ORIGIN of heritable variations is a fundamental aspect of the process of evolution. From the studies and conclusions of Darwin and Wallace considered in the preceding chapter, it is clear that any study of the process of adaptation must begin with an investigation of the sources of new, heritable variations. Although Darwin and Wallace each acknowledged their uncertainty about the mechanism of origin of individual variations, they were certain that such variations occur within populations. Darwin drew heavily upon evidence from domestic animals, and Wallace leaned more on examples from wild or natural species. In this chapter we shall briefly outline and discuss the general nature and sources of genetic variations. In following chapters we shall develop the role of natural selection as a variation-sorting agent which determines the genetic variants which are (or are not) favored. It is hoped that this discussion of process in evolution (Chapters 1, 2, and 3) will illustrate how adaptation of populations occurs by the operation of natural selection on individual genetic variations.

Before proceeding to an account of the origins of genetic variations, we will summarize briefly the conclusions and importance of the work of Gregor J. Mendel (1822–1884) on particulate genetic inheritance, first published in 1866. Mendel's work was independently rediscovered in 1900 by three geneticists: Hugo de Vries, Carl Correns, and Erich von Tschermak. As we have noted, Darwin and Wallace had trouble providing a mechanism for the passage of traits (we now say *genetic traits*) from parents to offspring. This was to come later with the publication of Mendel's work and its subsequent rediscovery. Mendel was born in Moravia, became a man of the cloth, and studied in his lifetime honeybees, meteorology, and inheritance in peas (*Pisum*) and other plant species. He discovered and presented experimental proof for the following principles:

1. The particulate nature of genetic inheritance.
2. The phenomenon of dominance of one gene over its allelic counterpart.
3. The principle of segregation of alleles during gamete formation.
4. The principle of independent assortment of genes during gamete formation.

The first three of these points can be seen in the hypothetical experiment illustrated in Figure 2·1. To describe natural selection we now use a different set of words and expressions from that used by Darwin and Wallace. Mendelian genetics are also described somewhat differently now. After acceptance and many confirmations as well as extensions of Mendel's work, a new series of nouns and adjectives was necessary. Bateson introduced such expressions as *genetics, zygote, homozygote, heterozygote, allelomorph* (= *allele*), and *factor*. The last word is equivalent to Mendel's *Merkmal*. This is the *gene,* a term first coined by W. Johannsen in 1909.

To evolutionists as well as geneticists not the least important finding stemming from Mendel's work is the demonstration of a mechanism which provides for stability as well as variability in hereditary factors. Thus various gene combinations are again and again made available

TABLE 2·1
Inheritance of Seven Pairs of Pea (Pisum) Alleles as Studied by Gregor Mendel

STRUCTURE	CHARACTER	DOMINANT	RECESSIVE	D/R RATIO
Seed	Form	5,474 round	1,850 wrinkled	2.96 to 1
Seed coat	Form	882 inflated	299 wrinkled	2.95 to 1
Seed coat	Color	705 grey	224 white	3.15 to 1
Cotyledon	Color	6,022 yellow	2,001 green	3.01 to 1
Flower	Position	651 axial	207 terminal	3.14 to 1
Unripe pod	Color	428 green	152 yellow	2.82 to 1
Stem	Length	787 tall	277 dwarf	2.84 to 1
	Total	14,949	5,010	2.98 to 1
	Percentage	74.9	25.1	

Source: G. Mendel, *Verh. naturforsch. Ver. Brünn,* 4:3–47, 1865.

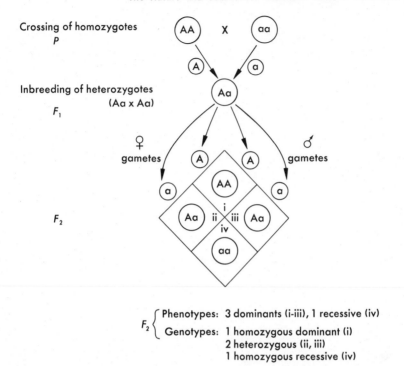

Crossing of homozygotes
P

Inbreeding of heterozygotes
(Aa x Aa)
F_1

♀ gametes   ♂ gametes

F_2

F_2 {
Phenotypes: 3 dominants (i-iii), 1 recessive (iv)

Genotypes: 1 homozygous dominant (i)
2 heterozygous (ii, iii)
1 homozygous recessive (iv)

Figure 2·1. A hypothetical experiment in which a homozygous dominant (AA) and a homozygous recessive (aa) individual are crossed in the parental generation (P). In the following, or filial (F_1), generation, only heterozygotes having the phenotype A are obtained. When members of this generation are inbred, or crossed with one another, a phenotypic ratio of three A to one a is obtained, and by subsequent crossings it can be shown that this phenotypic distribution masks in reality a genotypic ratio of 1:2:1. Here the genotypes are one AA, two Aa, and one aa. This experiment demonstrates the particulate nature of genes, dominance (with A masking a in the F_1 and part of the F_2 generation), and the random segregation of alleles. The latter point refers to separation of alleles, or sister genes, in gamete formation, with one allele going to one gamete and the other allele to another gamete.

for testing in natural populations by natural selection. A final point of interest about Mendel's work deals with the elegance and comprehensiveness of his experiments. (Of interest here is that R. A. Fisher has noted that Mendel's results are almost too good in a statistical sense; nevertheless the fact remains: he was right!) Mendel worked with large numbers of crossings, and practiced the deductive approach of testing a hypothesis against experimental results. Table 2·1 lists for seven different pairs of alleles controlling phenotypic attributes of peas the numbers of dominant and recessive individuals recorded by Mendel. The ratio of dominants to recessives is 2.98/1.0. Not a bad fit to a model of 3/1! It is of value to graph (see Figure 2·2) from his data the devia-

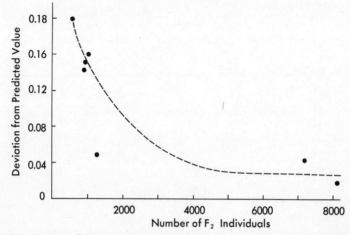

Figure 2·2. Scatter diagram. The graph shows the (roughly) inverse relation between sample size and the deviations from predictions by observed values for the seven pairs of alleles tested for ratio of dominants to recessive by Mendel (see Table 2·1).

tions from prediction against total numbers of F_2 dominants and recessives for each pair of segregating alleles. Prediction error is observed to decrease in correlation with increase in sample size, which serves as an excellent reminder to all of us of the necessity to work with large sample numbers in either laboratory or natural experiments.

The Nature of Variation

In nature two kinds of differences can be designated: variations among populations, races, or species; and variations among individual members of a population. We shall be concerned in this chapter with the latter or intrapopulational variations among individuals. Examples of the former so-called group variations will be taken up in Chapters 4, 5, and 6.

All sexually reproducing organisms vary. No two such individuals are exactly alike. A variety of factors contribute to the particular identity or specific measurements of a given individual. One may say that individual variations nearly always represent a resultant of nongenetic variation combined with genetic variation. Ernst Mayr and others have reminded us that as a crude generalization it may be said that nongenetic variation adapts the individual, while genetic variation adapts the population. Variation of the latter category is of major importance to the evolutionist.

Before going further, it is useful to distinguish clearly between *geno-*

type and *phenotype* in denoting individual traits or characteristics. Genotype refers to the sum or totality of the genetic attributes of an individual. Phenotype refers to the totality of characteristics which comprise the appearance of an individual; it results from an interaction between an individual's genotype and its internal as well as external environment. The two definitions are not natural opposites. Both genotype and phenotype are concerned in adaptation by natural selection, but only differences in genotypes are sources of heritable variations. Now because natural selection can operate only on the phenotype, it follows that only differences in phenotype with correlated differences in genotype are the substrate for natural selection. Differences among phenotypes having common or identical genotypes may provide variation for immediate selection (hence a form of adaptation of the individual), but the variations thus selected will not be inherited. Thus it is often stated that if genotypes vary, and if the phenotypes respectively reflect this genotypic variation, the materials necessary for adaptation by natural selection are present.

All individuals exhibit differences as well as similarities. Each human individual differs in quantitative or qualitative aspects of voice, body shape, gestures, and behavioral postures. Students of animal behavior are fond of saying that animals communicate by signals stemming from patterns in coloration, vocalizations, behavioral motions and postures, odors, and so on. That is, visual, auditory, and olfactory sensory and motor systems are used in various combinations and intensities by animals of different ecologies and environments to communicate information between one another. Most of us have at best a merely adequate knowledge of such communication for only one animal species—and that is man. It is thus not surprising that at a superficial level we think of our fellow human beings as possessing marked individual differences ("no two alike"), while considering individuals of animal species to be quite similar in appearance. This is primarily because we do not daily have contact with, and the regular use of, the particular communication systems of these other animal species. In the same vein of comparison, those of us who are members of one race of the species man (*Homo sapiens*) nearly always fall into the trap of assuming our kind of individuals to be delightfully variable, and those of other races of man to be monotonously invariable!

Animal behaviorists studying individuals of a given species soon learn to recognize specific individuals. Their studies have shown for many vertebrate species that individual recognition by the members is a real and usual event. For example, in the large breeding colonies of the monomorphic gulls (*Laridae*), an individual bird is able to recognize another as or as not its mate. The recognition here (unlike some other animal species) is direct, being mediated by specific recognition of the individual, and not by the indirect means of simply associating the mate with the occurrence of an individual on a defended territory or special area. These slight and subtle (at least to us) differences between individuals are one manifestation of the differences or variations which are the materials available to natural selection.

Continuing a discussion of the general nature of variations in individuals within populations, we may discern two kinds of intrapopulational variation. In one case, the variations are essentially continuous. Often they exhibit statistically a parametric or normal distribution around a population or sample-mean value. In the other case, individuals exhibit discontinuous variations or differences. Here individuals are discontinuously different from one another, with no intermediate situations existing. That is to say, each individual when measured for expression of a particular character falls either into one category or another. In this instance, there is not a continuous series of individual measurements with individual values rising, centering around an average, and then falling off in the typically unimodal manner. Examples of the discontinuous type of intrapopulational variation of individuals come under the complicated topic of polymorphism.

Many kinds of intrapopulational polymorphism exist, ranging from biochemical to morphological to behavioral polymorphism. Here is one example of biochemical polymorphism: human beings possess blood groups of various types. Each *individual* is either A, B, AB, or O. There are no intermediates. Alleles at a single chromosomal locus determine the ABO antigen for specific individuals. Polymorphic situations, with discontinuous gaps between genetic (allelic) variants are obviously much easier to study because of their readily quantifiable nature as well as their mostly complete genetic control. Continuous variations, such as exist for individual variations in body size or stature, are difficult to examine. These result from polygenic control as well as from the confounding problem of their having a joint genetic and nongenetic basis. This is sometimes referred to as the problem of *nature versus nurture.* Continuous and discontinuous variations between individuals within populations are of major importance in evolution. This is not to say that all examples of such variations are adaptive in nature. They are at least manifestations of the array of heritable variations on which natural selection acts, or can act. Additional examples of polymorphism and its role in the adaptation of individuals and populations to their environments are presented in Chapters 3 and 4.

Sources of New Variation

We have seen that variations in genotype with associated or correlated variations in phenotype provide the materials within populations on which natural selection operates immediately for adaptation and ultimately for evolution. The sources of these variations, following G. G. Simpson, may be summarized as follows:

1. Mutation:
    a. of genes.
    b. of chromosomes.
2. Recombination:
    a. of genes by crossing-over and segregation in meiosis.
    b. of chromosomes by conjugation of gametes with unlike chromosomes.

Truly new genetic variations arise only by mutation. Mutation is an incoherent if not random process which provides *de novo* changes in genes and chromosomes. Recombination, by far more frequent in occurrence, provides new individual variations within populations to a much greater degree than mutation. Indeed most of the individual genetic variations observed within populations are of a recombinational origin. But these are new variations limited to a range set by a preexisting genetic theme. New genetic themes arise only by mutation. To generalize, recombination provides *ad hoc* genetic variations of great importance in immediate adaptation and short-term evolution, whereas mutations provide *de novo* genetic variations of great importance in the long-range as well as short-term adaptation and evolution of populations.

GENIC MUTATION

To the extent that variations among individuals within a population are genetic, such variations may result from different genes at a particular point or locus on a chromosome. We designate such gene differences as follows:

$$\frac{a}{a} \; ; \; \frac{a'}{a} \quad \text{and} \quad \frac{a}{a'} \; ; \; \frac{a'}{a'}$$

The two alleles are denoted by a and a', and the horizontal lines ($=$) refer to the two members of a pair of homologous or "similar" chromosomes. In the usual course of events for sexually reproducing organisms, genes are reproduced and copied exactly during the meiosis or gamete formation. And although this chapter is chiefly concerned with the origins of individual differences within populations, it must be remembered that a major conclusion from Mendel's studies was the existence of a mechanism by which the Merkmal or gene is exactly duplicated.

Nevertheless, mistakes occasionally occur during the copying or replication of genes in meiosis. These mistakes represent *spontaneous mutation*. Once a mutation occurs (for example, $a \rightarrow a'$), it is then reproduced and copied exactly during meiosis, as if it were still in its original form. Geneticists in our century, working with the garbage or fruit fly genus *Drosophila*, have overwhelmingly demonstrated the phenomenon of spontaneous mutation. In fact all sexually reproducing unicellular, plant, and animal species that have been studied genetically have been found to exhibit spontaneous mutation. This includes, to cite only a few, bacteria, corn, mice, and man.

Genes are exceedingly stable units. But if studied carefully in large numbers and by means capable of discriminating between the presence of a mutant or that of its wild-type of allele, each gene is found to exhibit a certain small rate of mutation. In *Drosophila*, mutation rates for individual genes are exceedingly low. For example, A. Schalet examined 490,000 daughters of *D. melanogaster* for spontaneous visible mutations. A few mutants were detected, and on the average he found about six transmissible mutants per million gametes. Table 2·2 summarizes some estimates of mutation rates for an array of genes in man. Note that different genes have different rates of mutation.

Mutants are recurrent. That is, given a sufficiently large sample and large number of mutants studied, we can expect to find the same mutant occurring repeatedly. Spontaneous mutation is also reversible.

TABLE 2·2

Estimates of Rates of Mutation for Human Genes

NATURE OF GENE	CHARACTER PRODUCED BY GENE	AVERAGE NUMBER OF MUTATIONS OF ALLELE PER MILLION GAMETES
Autosomal dominant	Epiloia	10
	Chondrodystrophy	45
	Pelger's nuclear anomaly	80
	Aniridia	10
	Retinoblastoma	23
Autosomal recessive	Microphthalmos and anophthalmos	12
	Albinism	28
	Congenital total color blindness	28
	Infantile amaurotic idiocy	11
	Ichthyosis congenita	11
Sex-linked recessive	Hemophilia	32

Source: J. V. Neel and H. F. Falls, *Science*, 114:419–422, 1951.

When a mutation has occurred at a given locus, eventually that new allele may in turn mutate back to its original allelic form. This is illustrated quite simply:

$$a \underset{v}{\overset{u}{\rightleftarrows}} a'$$

Here a and a' are alleles at the same locus and the arrows denote their respective mutation rates (u, v) in either direction. Points of emphasis here are the spontaneous nature and reversibility of mutation. Although only two alleles are illustrated above, additional allelic mutations at a given locus are the rule and not the exception. Spontaneous mutation at individual loci gives rise to multiple alleles for genes. Geneticists have described genes possessing nearly fifty alleles, and the topic of allelic or genic polymorphism in natural populations is currently of considerable interest to population geneticists.

It should not be assumed that the mutation rate from any allele to another is the same for all possible mutational variants at a given locus. As different genes (Table 2·2) possess different rates of mutations, different alleles of the same gene have different mutation and back-mutation rates. Such observations and conclusions as these given in the last several paragraphs are what evolutionists have in mind when they talk about the random nature of spontaneous mutation. Whether this is truly random (for gene-to-gene comparisons) is uncertain. Nevertheless, spontaneous mutation is infrequent and unpredictable in terms of whether an allele mutates to one or another allelic state.

INDUCED MUTATIONS

To the evolutionist the matter of experimentally or x-irradiation-induced mutation is usually considered of little interest. That spontaneous rates of mutation can be accelerated to an induced category nevertheless underlines the unit nature of genes. It further reminds us of the dynamic aspect of gene occurrence. Individual genes or alleles within a population are at all times present in frequencies that—apart from effects of selection, gene flow, and random genetic phenomena—reflect an equilibrium between birth rate (= mutation) and death rate (= subsequent mutation at the same locus). We thus pay homage to the early investigations of H. J. Muller, N. W. Timofeeff-Ressovsky, and others for showing that rates of mutation at given loci can be brought experimentally under quantitative—but not qualitative—control. In summary, these and subsequent investigators have demonstrated that there is an apparent linear relation between frequency of mutation and the dose of x-irradiation applied to *Drosophila* individuals. A great deal of work has been done in the area of induced mutations, and it is now known that other external agents (such as ultraviolet irradiation), temperature extremes, and chemical agents (such as mustard gas) will also induce mutation.

CHROMOSOMAL MUTATIONS

For the most part the difference between genic and chromosomal mutation is one of degree rather than kind. A standard comparison of chromosomal mutation follows:

1. Numerical changes:
   a. nondisjunction: loss or addition of part of a chromosome pair.
   b. haploidy: loss of a pair of chromosomes.
   c. polyploidy: addition of one or more pair of chromosomes.
2. Structural changes:
   a. deficiencies: loss of a locus or loci.
   b. additions: duplication of a locus or loci.
   c. translocations: exchange of loci between different pairs of chromosomes.
   d. inversions: inverted loci sequence for part of one chromosome.

The factors and nature of spontaneous mutations of chromosomes in natural populations are even less understood than those causing spontaneous mutations. Plant and animal cytologists have documented the occurrence of individual differences in chromosome number and structure. The evolutionist is interested in chromosomal mutation at two levels: one deals with its role in the continuous origin of individual genetic variations within populations, and the other concerns its role in the origin of new species. Although this book is concerned only with evolution in animals, students should realize that polyploidy in plants produces a new species at once. The success or failure of polyploid species arising by mutation is immediate. Its fitness is tested by its local environment. This is an important way whereby new plant species arise.

RECOMBINATION

In sexually reproducing organisms there are nearly always two sexes. An individual of each sex produces germ cells or gametes. At the time of production the two sets of genes segregate in a manner which results in the gametes possessing one of the two sets of genes. When the gametes of two parents (sperm and egg) unite during fertilization, the two sets of genes are again paired. Because of segregation, independent assortment (see the account of Mendel's findings), and crossing-over, a great array of recombination of pairs of genes occurs by the mechanism of gamete formation and fertilization. If mutations have occurred during meiosis and gene copying, these mutations will of course segregate and be assorted independently. To cite a simple case, if ten mutations occur in an asexual, haploid organism, only twenty different phenotypes can be expected in the offspring. But if the organism possessing ten mutants is a sexually reproducing species exhibiting the phenomena of recombination, then 2^{10} or 1,024 phenotypes might be found among the offspring. Thus recombination at a given time period greatly increases the hereditary variability expressed in offspring over what could be expected if recombination did not occur.

The function of sexuality should be self-evident. It permits recombination and thus greater genetic variability for the population. Here it is helpful to return to the point that Mendel emphasized the particulate, rather than the blending, nature of inheritance. Stability as well as variability are characteristics of genetic material. Generation after generation the gene is stable; it mutates and then remains stable, until eventually it mutates again. Thus genetic material is conserved at a basic level. At an auxiliary level within any particular time period, the amount of genetic variations (= genetic variance) in a population is further increased through the recombination of genes.

Finally, students should not consider genetic recombination as a disorderly mixing of the genes of the two parental gametes. On the contrary, recombination is a stochastic process with elements of order as well as elements of chance determining the outcome. (By stochastic we mean that elements of chance as well as deterministic elements participate in the generation of the observations.) Segregation and independent assortment, as discovered by Mendel, are the elements of order. Mutation and crossing-over represent the elements of chance. But even crossing-over of genes is not really a mixing of genes. Rather the extent of gene exchange during crossing-over is governed by the extent of the chiasmata (see Figure 2·3) and the structural limits of the chromosomes participating. Genetic recombination is a truly recombinational mechanism, and not a haphazard mixing of genes.

GENIC SEGREGATION, CROSSING-OVER, AND CHROMOSOMAL ASSORTMENT

The following expression is useful to compare sources of variation by mutation and recombination: "mutation results in new genes; recombination takes the old and new genes and continuously produces new gene combinations." That is, recombination produces new genotypes. Figure 2·1 illustrates the operation of independently segregating alleles. Figure 2·3 describes how crossing-over of genes can occur during

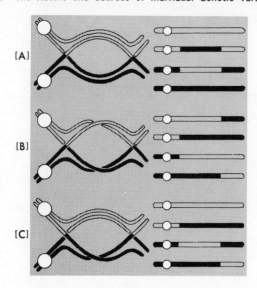

[A]

[B]

[C]

Figure 2·3. Examples of crossing-over. This figure demonstrates several ways that maternal and paternal chromosomes may, during pairing with one another, break and in turn exchange parts. **A:** Reciprocal chiasmata. **B:** Complementary chiasmata. **C:** Diagonal chiasmata. Each represents one pair of chromosomes.

meiosis when one member of a pair of homologous or similar chromosomes exchanges parts with its fellow. It should now be clear that crossing-over is a regular feature of meiosis. Chiasmata seem to occur at all points on the chromosomes, and in the simplest terms each unit of chiasmata and crossing-over increases by two the number of genetically different gametes that can result from the termination of meiosis. Another source of genetic variation is explained by Mendel's principle of independent assortment of nonhomologous alleles. This principle holds good only for pairs of alleles which occur on different chromosomes. Only alleles on the same chromosomes are affected by the recombination which results from the crossing-over and segregation occurring during meiosis. Independent assortment of chromosomes during gametogenesis or gamete formation results in differences in gene combinations for alleles on different chromosomes.

If we visualize mutation, genic crossing-over, allelic segregation, and independent assortment of chromosomes, and then imagine several thousand genes to each chromosome, remembering there are twenty-three pairs of chromosomes in man, we see that a sexual system is a mechanism for generating an astronomically large number of individual genetic variants. In reality, not all of these can be picked up by techniques of genetics. In these terms, the possible range of individual variations in gene combinations is extraordinarily wide, but is restricted by different degrees of the inborn, nonviable status of some variants, and by selection.

For a sexually reproducing population, it is useful to make a distinction between realized and hidden genetic variability. That is, variation can be divided into what is realized and what is hidden at any one point in time for a population under natural selection. Variation and variability are two expressions constantly confused by students. *Variation* refers to differences in measured or evaluated characteristics of the units compared. It refers to the array of differences between individuals within a population. *Variability* refers, however, to the capacity to vary. As used here, it means the ability—potential or real—of a population to vary. As will become clear in the following chapter, the variability of a population (that is, its ability to produce individual variations) is one measure of its potential ability to cope with and meet the demands of the consecutively different selection pressures which operate on it as a result of changes in the environment. In this sense, we think of variations hidden within the genotypes of the individuals comprising the population, and thus available in subsequent generations to natural selection.

One example of hidden variability is linkage. We call two loci or genes linked when they occur on the same chromosome. Such loci do not exhibit independent assortment. They are unlinked only by crossing-over, and population geneticists have found a variety of genic or chromosomal devices which prevent unlinking. In some cases cross-over inhibitors and inversions may prevent the disruption or separation of linked genes. From one viewpoint, linkage and enforced linkage are mechanisms for preservation of genetic variation. This is one introduction to the problem of hidden or concealed variability. In theory at least, the unlinking of linked alleles represents a means of realizing more genetic variation within populations. The problem turns on whether selection operates for preservation of certain linked alleles, or for disruption of those loci.

GENE FLOW

The topic of gene flow and its role in the adaptation of the population, in the speciation of groups of populations, and in related matters will be considered in following chapters. In this chapter we have been concerned with the sources of new genetic variations within populations. More specifically, we have seen how heritable variation is produced within a sexually reproducing population by the processes of mutation, genic segregation and crossing-over, and independent assortment of chromosomes. Gene flow from adjacent, related populations provides another means whereby new genes and gene combinations may be introduced into a given population. Gene flow stems from the active or passive dispersal into new environments of individuals adapted to their former environments. There they cross or interbreed with individuals of the local population, and thus exchange genes with individuals adapted to the new environment. In this way the gene pool of a population is enriched or diluted by the influx of what Ernst Mayr refers to as "alien" genes. For comparisons of the sources of new genetic variations manifested at the individual level, it is mandatory to understand that mutation and recombination *produce* genetic variations within a population, whereas gene flow *introduces* genetic variations into that population.

Conclusion

Mutation is ultimately the source of all new genetic variations. Recombination and gene flow are responsible for most of the new genetic variations observed at any one time in a natural population. Diversity of genetic variation stems from the instantaneous participation of new mutants in the normal Mendelian process of inheritance. The three kinds of genes found in a population—old, new or mutant, and alien genes—lead to greatly increased variation of genotype through the processes of genic segregation, crossing-over, and independent assortment of chromosomes. Thus a stochastic process is set in motion (according to the Mendelian principle of inheritance) for the continuous production of individual genetic variations. A large amount of genetic variation is the rule for natural populations. The question arises: To what extent is this genetic variation affected by natural selection and random genetic phenomena when a population is in the process of adaptation?

Further Reading

Dobzhansky, Th. *Genetics and the Origin of Species.* Third edition, second printing. New York: Columbia University Press, 1953.

Haldane, J. B. S. *The Biochemistry of Genetics.* New York: The Macmillan Company, 1954.

Mendel, G. *Mendel's Principles of Heredity.* Translated by J. A. Peters. Cambridge, Mass.: Harvard University Press, 1959.

Muller, H. J. "Artificial Transmutation of the Gene." *Science, 46:* 84–87, 1927.

Sturtevant, A. H. *A History of Genetics.* New York: Harper and Row, Publishing, Inc., 1965.

Timofeeff-Ressovsky, N. W. "Mutations and Geographical Variations." In J. Huxley (ed.), *The New Systematics.* London: Oxford University Press, 1940.

Waddington, C. H. *The Strategy of the Genes.* London: George Allen and Unwin, Ltd., 1957.

White, M. J. D. *Animal Cytology and Evolution.* Second edition. London: Cambridge University Press, 1954.

3

Natural Selection in Relation to the Genetics and Ecology of Natural Populations

The variations come first, the organisms do the best they can with them, and natural selection is the arbiter.
Sewall Wright (after Darwin), 1949, p. 365.

While examining the process of evolution by natural selection, we shall try to relate in this chapter two areas of biological or evolutionary inquiry: population genetics and population ecology. The approach will be mainly theoretical. Even when results of natural experiments or estimates of characteristics of natural populations are presented, the emphasis will be on theoretical interpretations of such studies. It is not necessary here to cover all the theories of population genetics and ecology. Rather, we shall discuss only that theory and those findings which have a direct bearing on the process of evolution in general. That is, we shall try to get a glimpse of how geneticists, ecologists, and evolutionists currently envision certain mechanisms. Through or by these mechanisms selection operates on populations to affect their genetic variations, thus bringing about shifts in gene frequency and associated gene replacement.

Genetics of Natural Populations

Population genetics and its mathematical basis rests mainly on the work of R. A. Fisher, J. B. S. Haldane, Sewall Wright, M. Kimura, J. F. Crow, C. C. Li, and D. S. Falconer. The theory of a genetical basis for natural selection starts with the fate of a single gene in a Mendelian population where individuals mate randomly in an idealized state of equilibrium. From this model, now to be discussed, follows the dissociation of the respective effects on gene frequency of mutation, selection, gene flow, and random genetic phenomena (genetic drift and the founder principle). These are the agents primarily responsible for alteration and adjustment of the genotypes, and genetic equilibria of natural populations.

THEORETICAL CONSIDERATIONS

EQUILIBRIUM AND GENETIC VARIATION IN THE ABSENCE OF MUTATION, SELECTION, GENE FLOW, AND RANDOM GENETIC PHENOMENA. A population where individuals mate or have the opportunity to mate at random is said to be in a state of *panmixis*. Panmictic populations are not frequent in nature, but in theory they provide a good point of departure for an examination of the adaptation of a population by natural selection. In such an examination, the expression *gene pool* is often used. The gene pool of a population is the sum or total of all genes occurring in that population at a given period of time. (One can speak similarly of the gene pool of an isolate, a race, or a species.) Using the single-gene model for a hypothetical population, it is assumed for a given locus that there are only two alleles present. Let a and a' be the alleles, and let n be the number of individuals in the population. If the members of the population are diploid and not haploid, the total number of genes present is n, and the total numbers of alleles is $2n$. The symbols p and q traditionally represent the fractions or frequencies of the total number of alleles for each allele. If we let x, y, z be the numbers of the three possible genotypes for the pair of segregating alleles $(aa; aa' = a'a; a'a')$, then the frequency of a is p, where

$$p = \frac{2x + y}{2n} = \frac{x + 0.5y}{n}$$

and the frequency of a' is q, where

$$q = 1 - p = \frac{2z + y}{2n} = \frac{z + 0.5y}{n}$$

We now turn to an account of the genotypic stability of a population which is in equilibrium for a particular gene or pair of alleles for other reasons than a balance of selection. Genotypic equilibrium in the situation here considered assumes random mating and the absence of mutation, selection, gene flow, and random genetic phenomena for the population concerned. It happens that if two different alleles (a and a') occur in three paired combinations and are reproduced exactly on a 1:1 basis—such as occurs in the Mendelian process of allele replication and segregation—the frequencies of the three paired genotypes will be the same in subsequent generations. This is true if there is random uniting of the gametes of the two sexes. Restated, if the three possible genotypes for a and a' occur in frequencies such that the genotypes aa, aa', and $a'a'$ are in the proportions of p^2, $2pq$, and q^2, then the population is said to exhibit genotypic equilibrium. This is the Hardy-Weinberg rule for equilibrium under random mating. It results from the occurrence of chance distributions agreeing with the binomial expansion which expresses Mendelian inheritance, where

$$(p + q)^2 = 1 = p^2 + 2pq + q^2$$

The maximum value for the heterozygote is 0.50, in which case the homozygote frequencies (p, q) are each 0.25. In this case, we write, for example, p^2 for aa is 0.25, pq for aa' is 0.50, and q^2 for $a'a'$ is 0.25, or 0.25:0.50:0.25. Here, $p = q = 0.50$ in a population demonstrating genotypic equilibrium under random mating, a change in allelic frequency (p or q) results in a symmetrical or ordered change in genotypic frequency. This is shown in Figure 3·1.

Polymorphism in the MN blood-group series for man provides an excellent example of this phenomenon. In Table 3·1, data are given for the distributions of the M, MN, and N phenotypes for several populations of man. In the case of a population of 208 Syrian bedouins, the results of blood tests are as follows:

$$
\begin{array}{rr}
\text{M:} & 119 \\
\text{MN:} & 76 \\
\text{N:} & 13 \\
\hline
\text{Total:} & 208
\end{array}
$$

Note that there are $2 \times 119 + 76$ or 314 M alleles, and $2 \times 13 + 76$ N or 102 N alleles in the population. The frequency (p) of the allele M is $308/308 + 102 = 308/416 = 0.75$. The frequency of allele N is $1 - p$ or 0.25. The expected frequencies for the three genotypes, MN, MN, NN can now be calculated:

$$
\begin{array}{lll}
\text{MM:} & 0.75 \times 0.75 = 0.56 \\
\text{MN:} & 0.75 \times 0.25 = 0.19 \\
\text{NM:} & 0.25 \times 0.75 = 0.19 \\
\text{NN:} & 0.25 \times 0.25 = 0.06 \\
\end{array}
\left.\right\} \, 0.38
$$

Following the Mendelian principles of independent assortment of chromosomes via random conjugation of gametes, we can calculate further:

$$
\begin{array}{lll}
\text{MM:} & 0.56 \times 208 = 117 \\
\text{MN:} & 0.38 \times 208 = 79 \\
\text{NN:} & 0.06 \times 208 = 12 \\
\end{array}
$$

The values 117:79:12 are a good prediction of the observed ratios of 119:76:13. (In most studies of this kind, predictions do not always conform to observed values; in that case we resort to chi-square analysis for tests of the degree of probability that the observed and predicted values are different.) Some students, thinking in terms of Mendel's $1:2:1$ genotypic ratio, might wonder why the M and N allelic frequencies are not each 0.5 and 0.5. This is true only in the rare situation where the two alleles are present in the population in equal frequencies. The data of Table $3 \cdot 1$ show the extent to which human populations vary in the frequencies of these two alleles.

Another aspect of this genotypic phenomenon at the population level is that, if two alleles are *not* present in the population in the proportions of $p^2 : 2pq : q^2$, then one generation of random mating in the absence of selection will establish a genotypic equilibrium with $p^2 : 2pq : q^2$ resulting. This will hold true for all subsequent generations, provided random mating continues. The student can prove this for himself. Simply select any three frequencies for the genotypes aa, aa', and $a'a'$ where the fractional sum is 1.0 or unity. Calculate p and q, and then determine

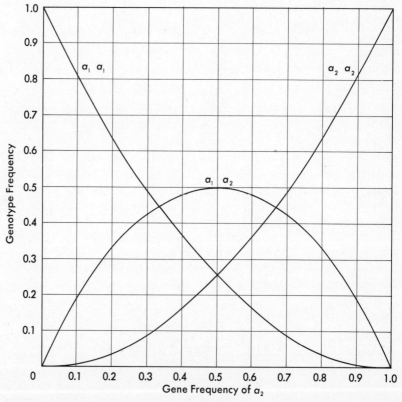

Figure 3·1. Relationship between genotypic frequencies and gene frequency for two alleles in Hardy-Weinberg equilibrium. [Source: D. S. Falconer, *Quantitative Genetics.*]

TABLE 3·1

Distributions of M and N Blood Type in Four Human Populations

POPULATION	NUMBER TESTED	PHENOTYPES OBSERVED			GENE FREQUENCIES		PHENOTYPES EXPECTED		
		M	MN	N	p(M)	q(N)	p^2(M)	$2pq$(MN)	q^2(N)
American Indian (Pueblo)	140	83	46	11	0.76	0.24	81	51	8
Brooklyn, U.S.A.	1,849	541	903	405	0.54	0.46	536	925	388
Australian aborigines	102	3	44	55	0.25	0.75	6	38	58
Syrian bedouins	208	119	76	13	0.75	0.25	117	79	12

Source: W. C. Boyd, *Tabulae Biologicae*, 17:230–235, 1939.

p^2, $2pq$, and q^2. Thus, if initial genotypic frequencies for a population are $0.1:0.1:0.8$, the genotypic frequencies after one generation of random mating will be $0.02:0.26:0.72$. (Note that here p is 0.14 and q is 0.85.)

A population in equilibrium may be visualized in another way by the use of homogeneous coordinates. This method is illustrated in Figure 3·2. Using Li's example, we see points (P) suspended in three-dimensional space. Since the sum of three perpendiculars to the sides of an equatorial triangle equals the altitude of the triangle, we let the altitude equal 1 and then (remembering that $p^2 + 2pq + q^2 = 1$) plot the frequencies of three genotypes to get our point in space. Another useful aspect of the equation $p^2 + 2pq + q^2 = 1$ is that it can be transformed to the equation $4p^2q^2 = pq^2$. This gives the hyperbola $4p^2q^2 - pq^2 = 0$, which when plotted by homogenous coordinates (Figure 3·3) provides a curving path on which fall the points of P for all populations in equilibrium. This is a vivid illustration of the internal consistency of the genetic equilibria that populations exhibit when their members mate randomly. Such equilibria are stochastic in process, being made possible by chance distributions governed by, or involving, as Li reminds us, the "symmetry of the Mendelian mechanism for bisexual reproduction."

EFFECTS OF SELECTION AND MUTATION ON THE GENES AND GENETIC VARIANCE OF NATURAL POPULATIONS. Before considering alleles that are selectively advantageous or disadvantageous, it is instructive to discover the fate of neutral genes or alleles. If an allele arises by mutation $(a \rightarrow a')$ and is of neutral selection value, it may easily be lost by chance alone. Here, neutrality in selective value means that the individual possessing the new allele (a') has a phenotype of neither in-

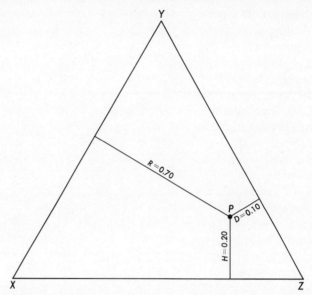

Figure 3·2. Homogeneous coordinates for a population point P when P = (D,H, R). In this case, D = p² = 0.10, H = 2pq = 0.20, and R = q² = 0.70. [Source: C. C. Li, *Population Genetics.*]

creased nor decreased survival value over that of a related individual possessing its allelic counter (*a*). R. A. Fisher calculated by the Poisson series the chances of survival over many generations of a gene or allele with neutral survival value, and compared that situation with a gene having only one per cent selective or survival advantage. Table 3·2 shows the progressive loss from a population of an allele of neutral survival value, and the slower loss of one with one per cent survival advantage. For the moment we might assume that most populations have their respective allelic frequencies adjusted by selection. Considering the so-called random nature of mutation, we can expect most mutations to influence the phenotype in a way which is disharmonious in interaction with phenotypic effects of other alleles. Such mutants will have decreased, or negative, survival value and will be selected out of the population rapidly. However, and here is the instructive merit of R. A. Fisher's calculations, even mutants of neutral value have small probability of remaining in the population over many generations.

At the time of his work, R. A. Fisher followed others in believing that the selective values of new mutants are relatively low in value. We now know this as something which may or may not be true. It depends on the nature of the new mutant as well as the nature of the environment and populations in which the mutant occurs.

Whether the allele is dominant or recessive is one factor that determines the rate of change in frequency of a given allele having a selective advantage in a population. That area of theory in population genetics dealing with the evolution of dominance and the origin of dominant genes is complicated and controversial. We will by-pass this topic and go on to more general ideas. Most new alleles arising by mutation are recessive to their allelic counterparts. This is by no means always the case. Some new mutants are dominants, and some are codominants. By codominance is meant the condition where both alleles when present in the heterozygote exert a distinguishable effect on the phenotype which is different from the respective phenotypes of either homozygous genotype. This relates to the problem of the origin of polymorphism and heterozygote superiority. If, however, the new mutant is truly recessive, it will be masked by the other dominant allele in the heterozygote. In this instance the new mutant is in part shielded from natural selection, because selection operates on phenotypes, and thus indirectly on genotypes. In this way, recessive mutants have slow extinction rates from populations when they are at a selective disadvantage. Recessive mutants are thus considered one class of contributors to the hidden variability or variation of natural populations.

Figure 3·4 compares the rates of change in frequency per generation for two alleles: one dominant, one recessive. With some oversimplification, the two curves illustrate the fates of two alleles within a Mendelian population. The alleles have the same slight advantage, but differ in

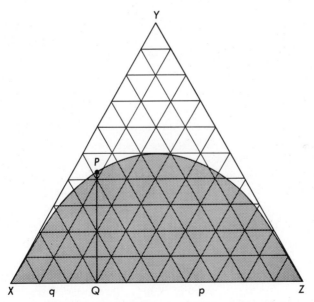

Figure 3·3. Parabolic distribution of population points (P) in equilibrium. PQ divides XZ in the ratio of gene frequencies (XQ = q; QZ = p). [Source: C. C. Li, *Population Genetics.*]

TABLE 3·2

Probabilities of Extinctions of Genes Having Neutral and One Per Cent Selective Advantage in a Population

NUMBER OF GENERATIONS	PROBABILITY OF EXTINCTION			PROBABILITY OF SURVIVAL	
	no advantage	1% advantage	DIFFERENCE	no advantage	1% advantage
1	0.3679	0.3642	0.0037	0.6321	0.6358
3	0.6259	0.6197	0.0062	0.3741	0.3803
7	0.7905	0.7825	0.0080	0.2095	0.2175
15	0.8873	0.8783	0.0090	0.1127	0.1217
31	0.9411	0.9313	0.0098	0.0589	0.0687
63	0.9698	0.9591	0.0107	0.0302	0.0409
127	0.9847	0.9729	0.0118	0.0153	0.0271
Limit	1.0000	0.9803	0.0197	0.0000	0.0197

Source: R. A. Fisher, *The Genetical Theory of Natural Selection,* p. 83, New York: Dover Publications, Inc., 291 pages, 1958.

genotypic dominance or recessiveness. Two points are noteworthy here. First, new mutants whether dominant or recessive increase more rapidly when their population frequencies are medium in value, and increase more slowly at higher frequencies. The rate of change in allelic frequency varies with the absolute frequency of the allele in the population, and is not constant for any given value of the coefficient of selection. Second, a mutant allele if recessive will also increase slowly at low frequencies.

Recent investigations indicate that selection pressures in operation on natural populations are of greater importance than theorists such as Sewall Wright and R. A. Fisher thought them to be. Selective advantages for alleles were calculated at the level of 0.5 to 1.0 per cent. Study of natural selection by investigators such as J. B. S. Haldane, S. Gershenson, E. B. Ford, and H. B. D. Kettlewell indicate to the contrary that selective advantages from 20 to 40 per cent are not uncommon. These findings (consider the example of industrial melanism in Chapter 4) show, as Ford has recently emphasized, that a population may adjust or adapt itself very rapidly to new selection pressures stemming from changes in its environment.

EQUILIBRIUM BETWEEN SELECTION AND EITHER MUTATION OR GENE FLOW. As a rule, natural populations are considered to be adapted to their environments to the extent that their genetic variance permits them to adjust to selection pressures. Mutation and gene flow can either promote or retard this adaptation of the population. Such a population is thought to maintain a certain level of equilibrium depending on the intensity of selection, frequency of mutation, and amount of gene flow occurring by immigration or emigration of related individuals from or to adjacent populations. By the single-gene model this equilibrium can be viewed in various ways. By one view, a gene is considered rare or common as a result of the equilibrium maintained by the mutation rate of the gene being balanced by selection, and counterbalanced in turn by (say) immigration.

As an example of a mathematical analysis of the agents responsible for changes in gene frequencies, we will consider D. S. Falconer's interpretation of selection, mutation, and gene flow as systematic processes operating in or on a large, random-mating population.

Natural selection involves the contribution of offspring to the next and future generations by one genotype rather than another. Selection obviously operates on the phenotype and not the naked genotype, but to the extent that there are correlations between genotype and phenotype, we will think in terms of selection of the genotype itself. The idea of increased or decreased contributions by one genotype to the next generation is subsumed by concepts of the *fitness, adaptive value,* or *selective value* of the individual possessing that genotype. The intensity

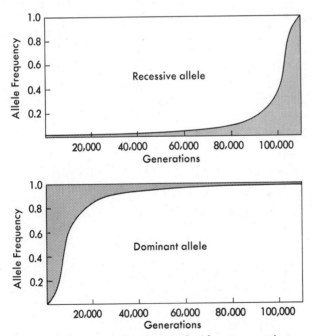

Figure 3·4. Rate of change in frequency of either a recessive or dominant allele. In each instance the allele has a selective advantage of 0.001, and its frequency varies from about zero to 1.0. [Source: C. Stern, *Principles of Human Genetics*, New York: W. H. Freeman and Company, Publishers, 1960.]

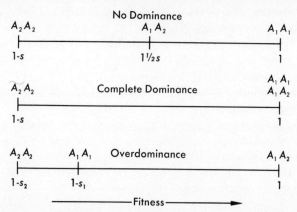

Figure 3·5. Degrees of dominance in relation to fitness. [Source: D. S. Falconer, *Introduction to Quantitative Genetics*, New York: The Ronald Press Company, 1961.]

of selection for an advantageous gene or genotype is set as 1 for a selection coefficient denoted by S, and that for a disadvantageous gene or genotype is considered to be $1 - S$. Because selection works on phenotypes, an account of effect of selection on phenotypes must consider the interactions of pairs of alleles on the phenotype itself. Examples of no dominance, dominance, and overdominance in relation to fitness are given in Figure 3·5. We will consider only the case of dominance for a single pair of alleles where a and a' have the initial frequencies of p and q. Here a will be dominant to a', and the coefficient of selection for the (assumed) disadvantageous genotype $a'a'$ will be S. We make the following quantifications:

genotype:	aa	aa'	a'a'	Total
initial frequencies:	p^2	$2pq$	q^2	1
fitness:	1	1	$1 - S$	—
gametic contributions:	p^2	$2pq$	$q^2(1-S)$	$1 - Sq^2$

Because selection is now in operation, the gametic contributions of the genotypes are no longer unity. The new gene frequency of a' is now

$$q_1 = \frac{q^2(1-S) + pq}{1 - Sq^2}$$

The change in gene frequency, Δq, for a' as a result of one generation of selection will be

$$q = q_1 - q_0 = \frac{q^2(1-S) + pq}{1 - Sq^2} - q_0$$

This can be reduced to

$$\Delta q = \frac{Sq^2(1-q)}{1 - Sq^2}$$

This shows us that the effect of selection on the frequency of allele a' is dependent on the initial frequency of a' as well as on the intensity of selection. For further development of this principle of selection, the student is referred to more detailed accounts of selection in texts on population or quantitative genetics. Here we will simply examine the results of a common intensity of selection on a dominance-exhibiting pair of alleles starting either with a high or low initial gene frequency of a' and an S value of 0.2. This is graphically explained in Figure 3·6.

To understand the effects of mutation on gene frequencies in natural populations, we will take the realistic model of recurrent spontaneous mutation. Here we will let p_0 and q_0 denote initial gene frequencies for a and a' having mutation and back-mutation rates as follows:

$$a \underset{v}{\overset{u}{\rightleftharpoons}} a'$$

In one generation with recurrent mutation, the change in frequency for the allele a' is

$$\Delta q = up_0 - vq_0$$

An equilibrium in gene frequency is easily seen. As the frequency of one allele increases by mutation, fewer of the other alleles are available for mutation in that direction, but more of the former alleles are in turn available for mutation in the other direction. The point of equilibrium

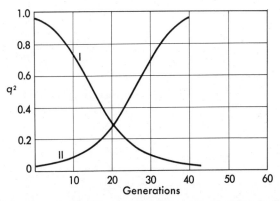

Figure 3·6. Change in frequency of a dominant gene with selection intensity (S) of 0.2 over forty generations. The graph marked *I* indicates selection against the gene, resulting in a decrease in q^2 or the frequency of the recessive homozygote. *II* indicates selection for the gene, resulting in increase in q^2. [Source: D. S. Falconer, *Introduction to Quantitative Genetics*.]

is determined by extrapolating the rate of change in frequency for $a'(q)$ to zero, where

$$pu = qv$$

and

$$\frac{p}{q} = \frac{v}{u}$$

and

$$q = \frac{u}{u + v}$$

Among the conclusions Falconer draws from such an analysis of the effects of mutation on gene frequency, of major importance to the student of evolution is the one that deals with normal mutant rates. These are thought to vary in the range of $1/10,000$ to $1/100,000,000$ gametes. By these estimates, it is clear that mutation alone can affect gene frequencies in natural populations only at a very slow rate. Conceivably mutation alone could be of importance in long-range evolution, but in no way that is possible could mutation account for the rapid population adaptations that the ecological geneticists have described. (This is discussed more fully in Chapter 4.)

Effects of gene flow resulting from the active or passive immigration of related individuals into a population are dependent on the proportion of immigrants to natives. For diploid organisms each individual immigrant carries one gene or one pair of alleles at each locus. Letting m and $1 - m$ represent the proportions of immigrants and natives in the population, we may assume for a given allele that q_m is the frequency for the immigrants and q_0 the frequency for the natives. At this first introduction of immigrants into the native population, the frequency of the allele for the resulting mixed population of genes (q_1) becomes

$$q_1 = mq_m + (1 - m)g_0 = m(q_m - q_0) + q_0$$

The change of gene frequency, Δq, resulting from one generation of immigration, is determined by the difference between the frequency before and after immigration. Thus we have

$$\Delta q = q_1 - q_0 = m(q_m - q_0)$$

Quite simply, the effect of gene flow on the rate of change in gene frequency in a population depends upon two factors: the rate of gene flow by immigration, and the extent of the differences in initial gene frequency between the immigrants and the native population.

We will ignore the mathematics describing establishment of genic equilibrium by a three-way interaction between selection, mutation, and gene flow. This is a complicated topic and for the purposes of this introduction to process in evolution we should do better to focus our attention on several self-obvious, but still important, conclusions from theory. By the single-gene model, it is evident that selection, mutation, and gene flow—when considered separately—affect gene frequencies in populations in ways determined by the initial gene frequency. For example, mutation is effective when the resulting mutant is rare or uncommon in the population. Thus gene frequency at any level of equilibrium reflects the mutation rate and the selection coefficient. It follows that if mutation rates are as low as geneticists tell us then weak selection will suffice to hold disadvantageous mutants at a low equilibrium level. Selection is effective in increasing the frequency of an allele when that allele is moderately common or frequent in the population. Selection is most ineffective when the allele is rare. Since the effectiveness of both mutation and selection in altering gene frequencies is dependent upon initial gene frequency, the two processes will produce a state of equilibrium if they operate continuously as well as jointly for a sufficient number of generations. The same conclusion holds for the joint or combined interactions of mutation, selection, and gene flow. And, theoretically, if we shift the source of new genotypes from mutation to a wider, more realistic field including recombination, then we can conclude that selection, mutation, recombination, and gene flow are four processes which strike an adjusted balance in natural populations to result in genotypic equilibrium. This is adaptation.

It is now time to make some conclusions from examination of hypothetical cases of adapting agencies affecting dominant or recessive alleles. To do this, we must consider the topic of heterozygote superiority. Here we deal with pairs of alleles where the heterozygote is superior in fitness in adaptive value to that of either homozygote. This is the case of overdominance, and the change in gene frequency after one generation of selection favoring the heterozygote is

$$\Delta q = \frac{pq(S_1p - S_2q)}{1 - S_1p^2 - S_2q^2}$$

When $q = 0$, equilibrium exists with $S_1P = S_2q$. Gene freqencies here are

$$\frac{p}{q} = \frac{S_2}{S_1}$$

or

$$q = \frac{S_1}{S_1 + S_2}$$

In short, where selection favors the heterozygote and the gene frequency is any value except 0 or 1, selection pushes that frequency toward the intermediate point of equilibrium. Thus both alleles remain in the population, buffered against extinction, so to speak, by heterozygote superiority in fitness or adaptive value. We now have a second definition of polymorphism (for the first, see Chapter 2). This is Falconer's: "The existence in a population of individuals with readily discernible differences caused by genes at intermediate frequencies. . . ."

EFFECTS ON GENOTYPIC VARIATIONS OF GENETIC DRIFT AND THE FOUNDER PRINCIPLE. Random genetic phenomena, such as genetic drift and the founder principle, are of uncertain significance in evolution and in the adaptation of populations to their environments. We will consider the theory behind each concept only briefly. Genetic drift refers to the effects of sampling error on the gene pools of small populations. Following R. A. Fisher and S. S. Chetverikov, Sewall Wright has developed this idea, the mathematical basis of which is quite sound. It involves the loss of genes due to sampling error when small populations of several hundred or less fluctuate to low levels (for example, ten individuals) in occasional generations. When the population is reduced temporarily some genes will be lost by chance, and the genes of the remaining few individuals will serve as the basis for the gene pool of the population as it springs back, increasing in size.

Some geneticists and evolutionists twenty to thirty years ago thought genetic drift to be a major evolutionary factor (though Wright himself did not always think so). In the last decade, the weight of opinion has shifted, and more frequently it is considered of inconsequential influence in the molding of the genetic attributes of small populations as well as in evolution in general. P. M. Sheppard in 1958, Ernst Mayr in 1963, and E. B. Ford in 1964 have all dismissed genetic drift as being of little importance in evolution. Ford in particular emphasizes that since 1942 selection pressures have been found to be normally of twenty per cent or greater, which indicates that even in very small populations selection at that intensity will overwhelm or counterbalance genetic drift in most instances.

One aspect of random genetic phenomena, essentially different from genetic drift, is Ernst Mayr's concept of the founder principle. This was first advanced in 1942 and further developed by him in an important essay in 1954. It has not received much attention from the mathematical geneticists (J. B. S. Haldane is an exception), but the ecological geneticists have found it useful in interpreting adaptation in small populations. The founder principle states that new isolates may arise outside the periphery of a species' breeding distribution in cases where new populations are founded by colonizers which are an atypical (but not random!) sample of the integrated gene pool of the parental species. Thus removed from the diluting effects of gene flow within the main body of the parental species, certain genes previously integrated and controlled by others have an opportunity for new expression on a new genetic as well as environmental background. Mayr believes that this situation may result in rapid changes in gene frequencies, permitting, as it were, a genetic revolution.

There is at least one way in which Mayr's founder principle can be related to the theory of population genetics. We have seen how the effectiveness of either mutation, selection, or gene flow in changing gene frequencies is determined by the initial frequency of the gene in the population. It was pointed out that selection, unlike mutation, is particularly effective when initial gene frequency is moderately high. On the periphery of a species' range new isolates or populations are constantly being established by founder individuals, and most probably become extinct in one or several generations. However, when one such population becomes truly established by virtue of freedom from predation, food shortage, parasites, and so on, the population may for several generations increase rapidly in numbers until limited by some factor in the environment. If novel genes or genotypes are carried by the individual original colonizers of the new population, they will occur after several generations of population increase with greater frequency than is usual in the parental species' population. Thus as the new isolate's abundance of individuals increases, selection pressures will have the opportunity to fix, or select for, genotypes with fitness geared to the new genetic and environmental background. Population ecology has now entered our discussion.

Ecology of Natural Populations

We will begin this account of some ecological properties of natural populations with quotations from the writings of two evolutionists:

. . . organisms automatically generate their own cycles of abundance and rarity and . . . the changes in selection pressures with which these are associated may greatly increase the speed of evolution.

E. B. Ford, 1964, p. 30.

The survival of the fittest will only cause the numbers of animals in an area to increase if the fitness concerns a negative density-dependent factor.

J. B. S. Haldane, 1953, p. 19.

We will return to the significance of these conclusions later, but first it is useful to relate the theory of population ecology to that of population genetics.

THEORETICAL CONSIDERATIONS

EQUILIBRIUM AND REGULATION OF ANIMAL POPULATIONS BY LIMITING FACTORS. Over short periods of time, species or populations rarely become extinct, and they rarely increase without limit. It follows then that populational as well as environmental factors interact in ways which increase populations when they are low, and decrease them when they are large. From the early writings of Malthus, Darwin, and Wallace, to the more recent ones of C. Elton, D. Lack, E. B. Ford, N. G. Andrewartha, L. C. Birch, F. M. Pitelka, and G. E. Hutchinson, it has been clear that environmental factors are limiting at certain levels of population size. Thus populations increase in size to a point where the environment supports no further increase. Because environments of populations are really never constant, it follows that population levels decrease when these factors become more limiting. Hence a balance is reached between the reproductive capacity of the population and the capacity of the environment to support individuals. An equilibrium zone is created, and from generation to generation a population fluctuates around this equilibrium. This introduces the topic of variation in the extent and form of population fluctuations. These fluctuations from generation to generation may be extensive, cyclical (Figure 3·7A), or erratic (Figure 3·7B). The student is referred to textbooks of ecology for discussions of population cycles, seasonal oscillations in abundance, and the rather complicated or confused interpretations of such phenomena.

Assuming a hypothetical situation, we say that for populations of

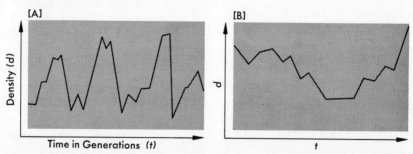

Figure 3·7. Schematic diagram showing two ways that the abundance or density of organisms may vary over a period of many years or generations. Such variations may be cyclical (A) or erratic (B). Note the importance of study of populations over a period of many years. Could not the so-called erratic fluctuation illustrated in B be merely a hollow or depression in a cyclical pattern such as in A, but occurring over a greater period of time?

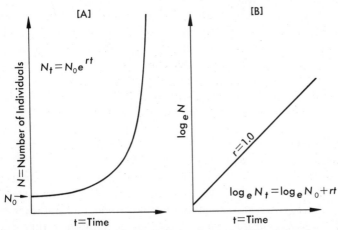

Figure 3·8. Exponential curve for population growth (N_t) starting from a given number (N_0) of individuals. A: Plotting of arithmetic values obtained by calculation of $N_t = N_0e^{rt}$. **B:** Calculation of the natural logarithm ($\log_e$) of N_t where $\log_e N_t = \log_e N_0 + rt$.

most species, the birth rate of each generation is essentially balanced by the death rate, and an equilibrium for population size or abundance of individuals exists. Population size or density is determined by these factors: birth rate, death rate, and loss or gain of individuals by dispersal. A valuable comparison can be made with the single-gene model of population genetics. We have seen that three factors in particular may change the frequency of an allele in a large, random-breeding population: intensity of selection, rate of recurrent mutation, and gene flow. Mutation gives birth to new genes in a population, gene flow from other populations adds alien genes to the population, and selection enforces a death rate on the old, new, and alien genes in the population. The analogy between regulation of gene frequency in a population and regulation of population size can be developed further. It will be shown that the theoretical rate of increase in a population size where limiting factors are nonoperative is determined in part by the initial size (N_0) of the population. We have seen in preceding paragraphs that the rate with which selection can change the frequency of a gene in a population is also determined in part by the initial frequency of that gene.

Although organisms rarely increase unchecked or unlimited by mortality, they do have the potential for exponential increase. This is described by the equation

$$N_t = N_0e^{rt}$$

where N_0 is the number of individuals, e is the base of natural logarithms, r is the instantaneous rate of increase, t is time. The exponential curve for such a population increase is illustrated in Figure 3·8.

Part of this curve can be seen (Figure 3·9) in the rise in number of ring-necked pheasants (*Phasianus colchicus*) over several generations following the introduction of the species on Protection Island, Washington. For the pheasant data given in Figure 3·9, the beginnings of a departure from the exponential curve and of an approach to equilibrium can be seen in the last generation. This could reflect a decrease in reproductive rate, an increase of mortality rate, or both. The weight of evidence would suggest that increased mortality is the best explanation. Components of mortality usually include predation (by man or other animals), disease, parasites, and food shortages.

Before studying the quantitative aspects of increase and stabilization of individual numbers, it is useful to consider what represents a stable population. This is one that maintains approximately the same size or the same numbers of individuals from one generation to the next. Restated another way, a stable population is in equilibrium in the sense that its annual or generation-time losses of individuals by mortality (= death rate = d) are equaled or balanced by gains or additions of individuals via the reproductive process (= birth rate = b). Thus the reproductive rate (r) of a population is equal to the birth rate minus the death rate. It follows, then, that stability occurs when b and d are equal (where $r = b - d = 0$). For increasing or decreasing populations, r will of course be > 0 (where $b > d$) or < 0 (where $b < d$).

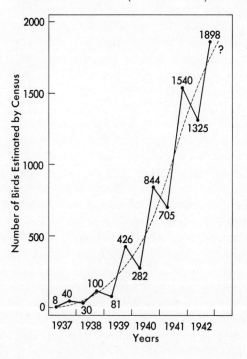

Figure 3·9. Increase in number of pheasant (*Phasianus colchicus*) on Protection Island, Washington, from 1937 to 1942. The population was sampled in the spring and fall of each year. [Based on data of A. S. Einassen, *Murrelet*, 26: 39–44, 1945.]

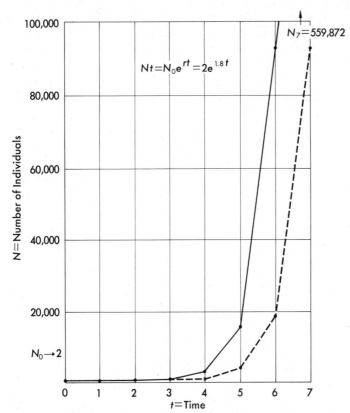

Figure 3·10. Hypothetical effects of seven years of population increase in pheasants happily feeding and breeding under no restraints from predation, disease, or sexual inhibition. Effects of strong predation or premature aging are shown by the slower second curve (broken line). For further explanation, see text.

THE EXPONENTIAL CURVE FOR POPULATION GROWTH. If problems are removed—problems of starving, finding mates, being taken by predators, getting diseases, becoming overly nervous because of too many or too frequent interindividual contacts, or anything working against survival and reproduction—then we may assume a survival period of ten years, clutch sizes of ten eggs, and regular, annual breedings of all females for the ring-necked pheasant. It is instructive to see what would happen if a male and female of this popular game bird were introduced into that hypothetical Elysian Field always favorable to reproduction and ecological requirements. Figure 3·10 projects over a period of seven years the exponential nature of the population explosion that follows the development of a population starting from two individuals in the hypothetical instance where the death rate is zero. By seven years the population numbers over five hundred thousand and by eight years, over three and a half million individuals.

The mathematics and their practical application are relatively simple, and for our discussion are given primarily for the purpose of determining the innate capacity for natural increase of individual numbers. Figure 3·10 represents a situation wherein one variable (number of individuals $= N$) increases progressively with another (time $= t$). This represents a curve of geometric increase in N with t. The rate of population increase (assuming constant age categories for births and deaths; for the pheasant example, deaths are zero) is given by

$$\frac{dN}{dt} = bN - dN$$

or

$$\frac{dN}{dt} = (b - d)N$$

Since $r = b - d$, then

$$\frac{dN}{dt} = rN$$

Integrating this differential equation, the exponential equation that results is

$$N_t = N_0 e^{rt}$$

Here, $N_t =$ number of individuals at time t, $N_0 =$ their number at zero, $e =$ the base $(2.71828 \ldots)$ of the Naperian or natural logarithm $(\log_e)$, and r the innate capacity for increase. In practice, to determine the predicted value of N_t it is easier to transform the exponential equation to its logarithmic form:

$$\log_e N_t = \log_e N_0 + rt$$

It is useful to remember that the term $\log_e N_0$ represents the $\log_e$ value of N at time zero. Furthermore, since $\log_e N_t$ plots against t in a linear manner, the simple regression line (r) intercepts the vertical axis where it is zero. Thus $\log_e N_0$ is the intercept value, a constant, and is sometimes replaced with the symbol a. For explanation of regression and correlation analysis, the student should see an introductory statistics textbook. Utilizing a table of natural logarithms (or remembering that the common logarithm of a number divided by the modulus, $0.43429 \ldots$, gives its natural logarithm), we can calculate $\log_e N_t$ as soon as r is determined. This is the rate of change of $\log_e N_t$ with change in t. In Figure 3·11, the r of Figure 3·10 is calculated by dividing the length of y by that of x to get 1.8, a pure number. Thus calculated, $\log_e N_t$ is transformed to N_t by the taking of antilog$_e N_t$ from a book listing such numbers and their transformations.

Returning to the pheasant example with its given conditions, the equation for its exponential growth is $N_t = N_0 e^{1.8t}$. The population's

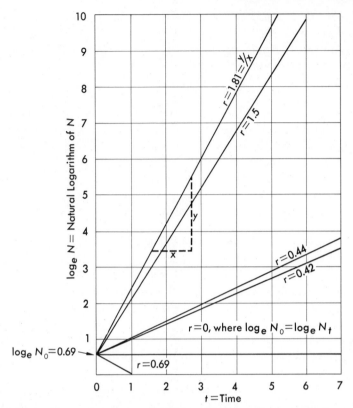

Figure 3·11. Effects of various population phenomena on population growth of the hypothetical example for pheasants discussed in Figures 3·9 and 3·10. For explanation, see text.

innate capacity for increase is 1.8, and the antilog$_e$ of this—6.11—gives the number of individuals increasing per female each year in the population. This is the finite rate of population increase (where $t = e^r$). Additional information on the rate of natural increase (r) and what controls its value can be obtained by varying hypothetically the biological characteristics and environmental conditions of the two pioneering pheasants. One might think that the high r value is caused primarily by absence of predation or to the successive annual reproductions of all individuals. Both of these possibilities can be considered at once. It can be assumed that all adults each year are so exhausted by amorous mating, excessive fighting, and the exhaustion of raising young, that their vigilance and awareness are unavoidably relaxed, and that all this permits a predator to wipe them out. A question may thus be asked, "What is r for the population if all adults are removed (by early aging or by predation) immediately after their one and only annual breeding, and after the raising of ten young per female?" Figure 3·11 shows that r in this case is 1.5. This is only slightly different from that for the first example, and the resulting curve for $N_t = N_0 e^{1.5t}$ is also plotted in Figure 3·10. This demonstrates that the only overall effect on the population growth when all adults are removed, by age or predation, after one successful breeding, is to delay by about one year the population explosion!

Consider the effect of 0.9 predation on the population result for the two individuals. r is decreased, but only to a level of 0.44. And if the individuals should die of old age at, say, 1.5 years (after breeding once), this, combined with 0.9 predation, reduces r only to 0.42. Finally, if predation and birth rate are such that a pair of parents on average see only two of their offspring through the maturation process to join the reproducing component of the population, then r is zero, and $\log_e N_0 = \log_e N_t$, and the population is balanced. Imagine how precarious a situation this is for a small population just getting started in a new environment. The effects of mortality can easily bring about the extinction of a new population possessing small numbers of individuals. But if the mortality rate is not high, the population can increase markedly in a few generations until other limiting factors operate to produce a zone of equilibrium.

DENSITY-DEPENDENT AND DENSITY-INDEPENDENT FACTORS REGULATING POPULATIONS.   The use of the word *factor* here is often confusing to the student. It is frequently useful to mentally replace this word with *situation* or *environmental situation*. Ecologists have for some time envisioned qualitatively density-dependent factors that decrease populations when they are too large in numbers, and that increase them when they are too small. An idea here has been that mortality factors are of two classes: one which is related to, or a function of, the population's density, and one which is independent (hence density-independent factors) of the population size or density. Examples of the first might include food supply, nest sites, space for defended territories; for the latter class we can cite seasonal extremes in temperatures, catastrophes, and so on. The distinctions do not always hold true, and there are, as usual, intermediate situations. J. B. S. Haldane, along with A. J. Nicholson, V. A. Bailey, and G. C. Varley, has brought some refinements to interpretation of density-dependent factors. Haldane makes a distinction between *negative* density-dependent factors, which decrease populations in general, and *positive* density-dependent factors, which increase populations when they are at a critically low level. As an example of the latter, colonial situations might be cited. Here frequently one pair, or a few pairs (larvae of fly, gulls) may not be able to survive or reproduce, but with more individuals or pairs present in a colony, individuals can obtain food or the behavioral stimuli necessary for survival and reproduction.

Competing species, food shortages, and fellow population individuals are common negative density-dependent factors. These factors, or the situations they induce, limit the numbers of individuals in natural populations. Haldane makes the point, quoted at the beginning of this chapter, that natural selection can cause an increase in the numbers of individuals of a population or a species only if it operates for increase in fitness of individuals so that they overcome these limiting or density-dependent factors. The latter are neither adaptations nor specific attributes of the environment; they are in fact situations of interactions between the population's individuals and their environment. Negative density-dependent situations result in mortality of individuals within populations, and only if there are genotypic differences between individuals selected to die and those reciprocally selected to live does this density-dependent induced mortality become a selective agent of the population's environment.

Finally, it is necessary to relate this discussion to that aspect of the Darwin-Wallace concept of natural selection which deals with organisms producing more offspring than can survive (see Chapter 1). Consider two models for a stable population, each of which results in $r = 0$: (Model I) the number of offspring produced (seeds, eggs, littermates) *equals* the loss of nonoffspring (old juveniles, adults) individuals from the population; (Model II) the number of offspring produced by the reproductive process is greater than in Model I, but only a fraction of these join as new juveniles the population of old juveniles and adults, thus equalizing the loss of individuals resulting from mortality. The first model having, say, the birth rate adjusted *directly* to the death rate is unrealistic. The second model is the realistic one, and its bearing on the theory of natural selection is obvious because by permitting more offspring than survive, it raises the possibility of differential survival of individual genotypes. It is important to remember that Model I does not preclude the operation of natural selection. There would still be genetic differences between those living and those dying each year or generation. Natural selection here would cease only in the limiting situation where all parents die, and are then replaced by an equal number of offspring produced. Nearly all plant and animal species are representatives of Model II. One species, man, may eventually shift from Model II to Model I, but let us hope if this is to come we are not forced into the limiting case of the latter model.

Equilibrium and the Natural Regulation of Species Abundance

Ecologists such as J. C. Willis, C. B. Williams, and F. W. Preston have studied in some detail the relation between numbers of species and the area of the islands on which such species occur. In Figure 3·12, we see such a species–area relation. The theory here is that as the sample area increases the number of species is increased by some function of the area. Recently various ecologists have begun to consider species ecology from the viewpoint of equilibria maintained by interaction between different, sometimes conflicting agents of the environments. Among these workers are R. H. MacArthur, E. O. Wilson, T. H. Hamilton, and I. Rubinoff.

In Figure 3·13 is shown the progressive decline from New Guinea outward in the number of land bird species native to various islands. These questions may be asked about the decline: is this a result of increased isolation or water-gaps decreasing dispersal of species to the far islands; is this a result of decrease in insular area with increased isolation; is this a result of the ecologically depauperate nature of the more isolated island; or do combinations of these possibilities account for the decreasing trend of insular variation in species numbers? Two equilibrium theories for explaining such insular variation in species abundance will now be compared.

MacArthur and Wilson have reasoned that the number of species on an island results from an immigration rate of species by dispersal being

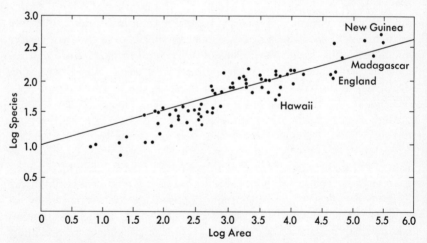

Figure 3·12. Relation between numbers of bird species and insular area for more than one-hundred islands, showing the apparent linear relation between area of islands and the number of land-breeding bird species. The straight line represents F. W. Preston's theoretical species-area curve (species number = 10 × area$^{0.27}$). Note the tendency for islands of small area to have fewer species than his equation predicts. Does this suggest that below a certain size there is a marked decrease in ecologic diversity, thus disproportionately reducing the number of species the island can support? (See text.)

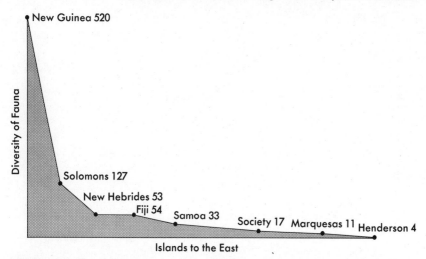

Figure 3·13. The progressive decrease among Pacific islands in size of insular avifauna with increased distance (isolation) from New Guinea. [After E. Mayr, *Proceedings, Sixth Pacific Science Congress, 4*: 197–216, 1940.]

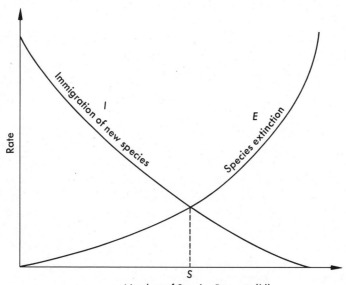

Figure 3·14. The MacArthur-Wilson equilibrium model for the fauna of a single island. S denotes equilibrium number (N) of species where the rate of immigration (I) is balanced by the rate of extinction (E). [After R. H. MacArthur and E. O. Wilson, *Evolution, 17*: 373–387, 1963.]

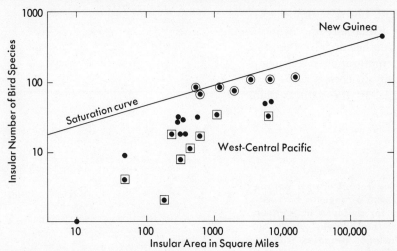

Figure 3·15. Relation between number of breeding bird species and insular area for some Pacific islands. The effect of isolation is estimated by linear distance from New Guinea, a major avifaunal source region. Near islands, less than 500 miles from New Guinea, are enclosed in circles (○); intermediate islands, 500 to 2,000 miles in isolation, are left unclosed (●); and far islands, isolated more than 2,000 miles, are enclosed in squares (□). Note that species numbers increase more rapidly with area on the more isolated islands. [After R. H. MacArthur and E. O. Wilson, *Evolution*, 17: 373–387, 1963.]

balanced by an extinction rate of species on that island. (In this case they essentially ignore the birth of a new species on individual islands, a factor which is probably of greater importance on large islands and continents.) Figure 3·14 shows such an equilibrium model for a single island. The intersection of the immigration and mortality curves provides a prediction for the numbers (N) of species to be found on the island. By this model the number of species for an island will be decreased by any aspect of insular environment which increases extinction rate of species (small area, severe climate), or decreases the immigration rate to the island (increased isolation, wind or water currents against dispersal). Their model (for its application, see Figure 3·15) is fairly consistent with the observed decrease in size of avifauna on islands in the Pacific, and it is useful to relate their findings to Mayr's demonstration that species become extinct on small islands more rapidly than on larger ones (Figure 3·16).

Hamilton and Rubinoff have proposed an equilibrium model that, following Haldane's conclusion, assumes extinction of species to be relatively infrequent in nature, and thus a minor factor in controlling variation in insular number of species among islands. Their model is predictive (see below) and suggests that insular avifaunal size is regulated by equilibrium established between isolation and the ecologic diversity of an island. In other words, immigration brings new species to an island, but the number of species the island can support is limited by the availability of ecological niches. Isolation (distance from one island to another or from the source of colonization) is taken as an estimate of immigration rate; area and elevation are taken as estimates of diversity in ecological niches. Figure 3·17 shows the application of the model to the data available for variation in numbers of land bird

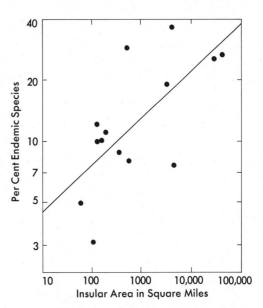

Figure 3·16. Evidence that the per cent of endemic bird species for avifauna of fourteen islands of various oceanic archipelagos increases with increase in insular area. This is interpreted as indicating increased extinction and turnover (hence reduced per cent of endemism) of avifauna on smaller islands. [After E. Mayr, *Science, 150:* 1587–1588, 1965.]

species among the islands of the Gulf of Guinea off west-equatorial Africa. It gives near-perfect prediction of each island's number of species. Multiple regression analysis is used in such studies, and students are urged to seek textbooks of statistics for accounts of this form of multifactorial analysis. In studies of this nature two statistical models (among others) are available, one is linear and uses arithmetic values, and the other is nonlinear, using common logarithms:

Single regression

    Model I   Model II

    $\hat{y} = bx$ $\hat{y} = bx^z$

    or   or

    $\hat{Y} = a + bX$ $\log \hat{Y} = \log b + z \log X$

Multiple regression

    Model I $\hat{Y} = a_{12} + b_1 X_1 + b_2 X_2 \ldots$

    Model II $\log \hat{Y} = \log b_{12} + z_1 \log X_1 + z_2 \log X_2 \ldots$

Here $\hat{Y}$ is the predicted numbers of species, a and $\log b$ are the respective intercept constants, b and z are the respective regression or partial

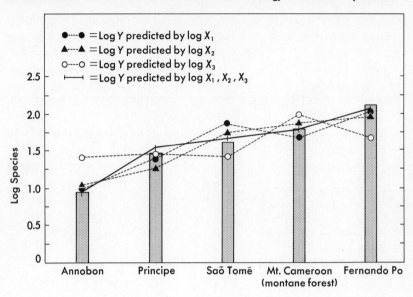

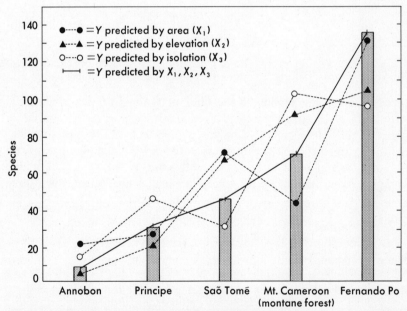

Figure 3·17. Prediction by knowledge of environmental factors (area, elevation, and isolation) of the number of breeding bird species occurring on four islands and Mt. Cameroon (on the mainland coast) in the Gulf of Guinea. Either by Model I or Model II (see text) good predictions of the reported numbers of species can be obtained. [After T. H. Hamilton and N. E. Armstrong, *Nature, 207:* 148–151, 1965.]

regression coefficients (estimates of rates of increase), and X and log X are the independent variables, or environmental factors used to predict $\hat{Y}$. In Model I, incidentally, $\hat{y} = bx$ represents in reality $y = bx^z$, where $z = 1$. In Model II, therefore, z does not equal unity.

The two equilibrium models considered are alternative approaches to species ecology. The advantage of the MacArthur-Wilson model lies in its conceptual elegance. It starts from statistical or mathematical theory, and then predicts (apparently) facts of nature. The Hamilton-Rubinoff theory has the advantage of a common-sense or utilitarian nature. It starts from ecological theory, takes the facts of nature, and then checks them against the theory. While the two models are not mutually exclusive, a point of difference involves whether or not the far islands of the Pacific are in fact saturated for their respective avifaunas. Hamilton and Rubinoff argue that these islands are depauperate in their nonavian ecology, and thus are deficient in ecological niches for bird species. In this sense these islands may well have saturated avifaunas for their particular ecologies. It is believed that in time most bird species disperse to the various islands of the Pacific, but that the ecological niches of these species have not yet dispersed to these islands! Thus the apparent effect of isolation on insular dispersal of bird species may result from effects on dispersal of species of plants and insects—organisms on which the birds are dependent for ecological support and successful colonization.

Finally, what bearing, the student may ask, has natural selection on species ecology or the abundance of species on islands? We answer by turning the question around: species abundance has a bearing on natural selection! Competing species are major negative density-dependent factors and thus are elements of the natural selection that operates on individuals of species.

Conclusion

This chapter may be concluded with a unifying idea which transcends the hierarchy of organic organization considered here: the gene → the individual → the population → the species. We think of populations of genes, populations of individuals, and sometimes populations of species. We rarely think, perhaps unfortunately, of populations of populations. At least for gene frequency, abundance of individuals in populations, and abundance of species on islands, equilibrium theories can be used to explain their respective regulations. In each case the equilibrium stems from balancing and counterbalancing agencies which may be categorized as unit-increasing processes (mutation, birth, or speciation), unit-decreasing processes (selection, mortality, or extinction) and unit-transferring processes (gene flow, immigration, or emigration). Different combinations of these processes, or interactions of their rates, determine the equilibria. The chapter represents an attempt to unify some elementary principles of population genetics, population ecology, and species ecology.

Further Reading

Cole, L. C. "The Population Consequences of Life History Phenomena." *Quarterly Review of Biology, 29 :* 103–137, 1954.

Elton, C. S. *Animal Ecology.* London: Sedgwick and Jackson, Ltd., 1927.

––––––. *The Ecology of Invasions By Animals and Plants.* London: Methuen, 1958.

Falconer, D. S. *Introduction to Quantitative Genetics.* New York: The Ronald Press Company, 1960.

Fisher, R. A. *The Genetical Theory of Natural Selection.* 1929. Second revised edition. New York: Dover Publications, Inc., 1958.

Ford, E. B. *Ecological Genetics.* New York: John Wiley and Sons, Inc., 1964.

Haldane, J. B. S. *The Causes of Evolution.* New York: Harper, 1932.

––––––. "Animal Populations and Their Regulation." *New Biology, 15 :* 9–24, 1953.

Hamilton, T. H., R. H. Barth, Jr., and I. Rubinoff. "The Environmental Control of Insular Variation in Bird Species Abundance." *Proceedings U.S. National Academy of Science, 52 :* 132–140, 1964.

Lerner, I. M. *The Genetic Basis of Selection.* New York: Wiley, 1958.

Li, C. C. *Population Genetics.* Chicago: University of Chicago Press, 1955.

MacArthur, R. H. "Patterns of Species Diversity." *Biological Reviews, 40 :* 510–533, 1965.

MacArthur, R. H., and E. O. Wilson. "An Equilibrium Theory of Insular Zoogeography." *Evolution, 17 :* 373–393, 1963.

Mayr, E. "Change of Genetic Environment and Evolution." Pp. 157–180, in J. Huxley, A. C. Hardy, and E. B. Ford, eds., *Evolution As a Process.* London: George Allen and Unwin, Ltd., 1954.

Slobodkin, L. B. *Growth and Regulation of Animal Populations.* New York: Holt, Rinehart, and Winston, 1961.

Williams, C. B. *Patterns in the Balance of Nature.* London: Academic Press, 1964.

Wright, S. "Adaptation and Selection." Pp. 365–387, in G. L. Jepsen, E. Mayr, and G. G. Simpson, eds., *Genetics, Paleontology, and Evolution.* Princeton: Princeton University Press, 1949.

Adaptations: Patterns in the Response of Populations to Natural Selection

I . . . define selection . . . as anything tending to produce systematic, heritable change in populations between one generation and the next.
                                                    G. G. SIMPSON, 1953, p. 138.

IN THE PRECEDING three chapters we have examined the Darwin-Wallace concept of natural selection, the origins and sources of new genetic variations, and some theories of population genetics and ecology. In Chapter 3, an emphasis was placed—either for the frequency of a gene in a population, for the number of individuals comprising a population, or for abundance of species on an island—on the establishment of equilibria for the units involved. Rates of mutation, selection, and gene flow were considered as interacting factors resulting in a particular equilibrium for the frequency of the gene in the population. Regulation of population size, birth rate, mortality, and emigration or immigration were the factors which, balancing or counterbalancing one another, determine the population size from generation to generation. The numbers of species on islands were shown to be the result of various interactions between isolation, immigration, extinction, and ecological characteristics of the islands. Because it breaks equilibrium and causes a shift to another level of equilibrium, the process of gene substitution or replacement was taken as the unit process in the adaptation of a population. Natural selection was observed to increase the numbers of individuals in a population only if it involves a negative density-dependent situation. This is a striking reminder that the natural regulations of a population and of its adaptation are not necessarily concomitant processes. A population can increase in numbers without an alteration in gene frequency. Conversely, the frequency of a gene can change without an alteration in the size of a population. Still again, both population size and gene frequency can increase or decrease together. The determining factor is whether or not the mortality enforced upon individuals coincides with decreased fitness for the phenotypes the genotypes of which pay the price of the mortality. We shall now consider natural selection on a more empirical basis. From this we will depart to specific examples of adaptations, or trends in evolution.

Selection Pressures

In this chapter we will follow Simpson's definition of selection as anything producing systematic, heritable changes in populations. The element of differential reproduction for genotypes where the phenotypes are favored by natural selection will be emphasized, and the Darwin-Wallace emphasis on differential mortality will be played down. By and large, the action of natural selection is to increase the effectiveness of the reproductive adaptations of populations. More accurately, natural selection adjusts the reproductive efficiency of populations to meet the restrictions placed on them by the constant change in their environments. The question arises: how does natural selection alter the genotypic structure and statistical character of a population to bring about adaptation? In theory this has been demonstrated in Chapter 3 where the process of gene substitution by selection was illustrated. We will now look again at the problem in a more empirical way.

EMPIRICAL CONSIDERATIONS

THE NATURE OF NATURAL SELECTION. It is to Darwin and Wallace, as we have seen, that we primarily owe the concept that adaptation and evolutionary change occur by the accumulation and summation of minor or small genotypic changes. Contemporary evolutionists say that natural selection results in the differential reproductions of the units of selection. It begins with interaction between environment and a recombinational array of phenotypes, and ends with an increase in reproduction or survival value for those genotypes the phenotypes of which have been positively selected. A point of clarification is useful here. Frequently it is said that natural selection *is* differential reproduction. Although this may be a rather fine distinction to make, to say that selection *results* in differential reproduction is more accurate. The emphasis on result focuses attention on the sequential nature of the interaction between environment and the phenotypes of the genotypes that comprise the units of natural selection.

Enhancement of survival value can be achieved by one and/or the other of the following adaptive responses: (1) increased rate of reproduction; (2) decreased vulnerability to environmental agents responsible for mortality. Competing individuals would also be included among the environmental agents here noted. The two responses achieve the same result: one alters the organism in a way which *increases* the birth rate over the existing death rate; the other alters the organism in a way which, without affecting the birth rate, *decreases* the death rate. The definitions given above turn on Darwin's and Wallace's concept that in a given environment some individuals will be more fit than others. Those individuals thus favored by the environment will contribute more offspring to the next generation. They will thus increasingly replace the less fit ones. In this sense, natural selection results in the passage of some genotypes into succeeding generations to a greater extent than for other genotypes. (It should be clear to the student here that for sake of clarity an unrealistic model is taken where for each genotype there is a specific phenotype.) This description of natural selection deliberately emphasizes the *reproducing individual* as the unit of natural selection.

What are the requirements for natural selection as a process? An abstracted list of requirements might go as follows:

1.   Units capable of reproduction.
2.   Occurrence of heritable variations or differences among these units.
3.   The testing of more than one such unit *within* the same environment.

Points 1 and 2 should be self-evident from Chapters 1, 2, and 3. Point 3 is most important. Two different genotypes must perform in the presence of the same selection pressure, or a common environment. For if one unit is to be more fit than another, then the other unit must be found less fit in the same environment. Otherwise, there can be no guiding of specific genotypes into future generations. Finally, the wide meaning of the word *environment* should be defined. Environment as employed in this book refers to all that impinges upon each individual's (or phenotype's or genotype's) ability to produce offspring. This includes conspecific individuals (or members of the same species), along with the more familiar elements of an individual's biotic environment.

THE DIRECTION OF NATURAL SELECTION.   According to Simpson's definition of selection, it follows that there must be direction in the operation of selection. That is, a process which ends in systematic, heritable change in a population must have shifted the genotypic structure and statistical character of that population from one state to another. Simpson points out that in these terms selection is a vector and thus has the characteristics of intensity and direction. We have considered intensity of selection. The expression of direction may be centripetal, linear, centrifugal, or an interaction of these. Figure 4·1 shows examples of selection where both intensity and direction of selection vary. There are many ways that types of selection can be so alternatively viewed. The relative importance in adaptation of these natural routes of selection is another problem. We will do no more than survey these routes and the attitudes that various evolutionists take in describing them. For instance, K. Mather and J. M. Thoday have emphasized the classification of stabilizing, directional, and disruptive selection. In Figure 4·2 these three natural routes of selection are outlined. Ignoring disruptive selection, which pushes phenotypes within a population away from the population mean, we will pay attention to the more common (but not necessarily the more important in evolution) examples of stabilizing and directional selection. In brief, stabilizing selection emphasizes the average phenotype and selects against either extreme phenotype. Directional selection favors one phenotypes which is non-average or extreme, and thus pushes the population of phenotypes (and their genotypes in turn) in the direction of that phenotype by selecting against the others. This is what has happened in the domestication of plants and animals. Man has here applied artificial directional selection.

STABILIZING SELECTION. Karn and Penrose examined from hospital

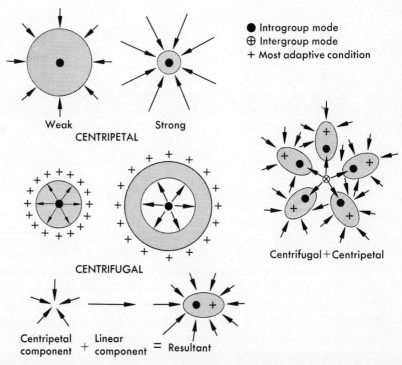

Figure 4·1. Direction of selection in relation to intensity, showing the theoretical possibilities of a centrifugal, centripetal, linear, or resultant selection. The shaded areas represent ranges of variations covered by the populations. [After G. G. Simpson, *The Major Features of Evolution*, New York: Columbia University Press, 1953.]

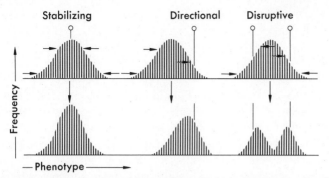

Figure 4·2. K. Mather's illustration of the three basic types of selection—stabilizing, directional, and disruptive. See Figure 4·1 and the text. [After K. Mather, *Symposia Society Experimental Biology, 7: 66–95*, 1953.]

records taken between 1935 and 1946 the weights at birth of 13,730 babies born in London. Of these, 614 were dead at birth, or died within the first month following birth. Figure 4·3 describes the relation between survival and weight at birth. There is evidence here of increased infant mortality for very small and very heavy weights at birth. This appears to be an example of centripetal (according to Simpson) or stabilizing (according to Mather and Thoday) selection, with both extremes of phenotypes being at a selective disadvantage. Haldane has considered this example and points out that for the population of babies considered, about 8 pounds is the optimum weight. At this weight, 1.8 per cent of the babies died. Because 4.5 per cent of all babies died, the

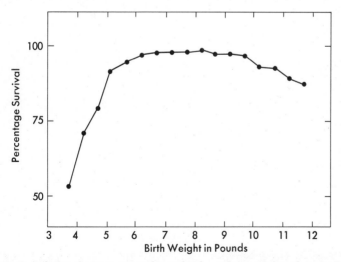

Figure 4·3. Relation between weight at birth and survival in human babies. [After M. N. Karn and L. S. Penrose, *Ann. Eugen., London, 16: 147–164*, 1951.]

difference between the two figures, 2.7 per cent, provides an estimate of natural selection for weight at birth. Selection intensity here would then be approximately 0.027. After noting the general occurrence in nature of centripetal selection on populations, Haldane humorously mimics Darwin's critics by stating (1959, pp. 123–124) how they might use such findings to deny the concept of evolution by natural selection: "In view (of these) findings Mr. Darwin's absurd speculations may now be relegated to the obscurity from which they should never have emerged. He postulated the existence of natural selection to account for the evolution in whose existence he believed. He doubtless deserved some credit for stimulating others to carry out accurate measurements. Natural selection was in fact found to occur. But so far from causing species to change, it actually prevents such change. Not only does it preserve the type of a species by eliminating deviants. It eliminates hybrids between species, which, if they are not too weak to be capable of development, are sterile."

DIRECTIONAL SELECTION. Good examples of directional selection are to be found in studies of artificial selection, and we will wait until later in this chapter to take up examples in nature. D. S. Falconer, whose work and thinking we have encountered, selected mice for low and high weight at six weeks of age. This is illustrated in Figure 4·4 for results of response to selection in eleven generations, and in Figure 4·5 for results in twenty generations. This is *phenotypic selection;* it

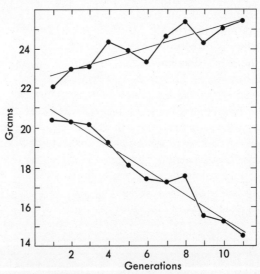

Figure 4·4. Two-way selection for body weight in mice—upward and downward. See text for explanation. [After D. S. Falconer, *J. Genetics, 51:* 470–501, 1953.]

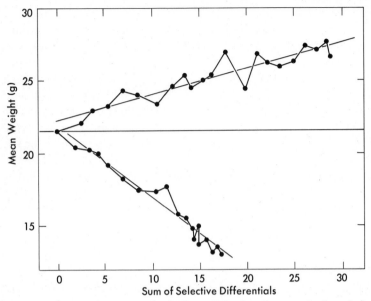

Figure 4·5. Two-way selection for body weight in mice—upward and downward—showing the relation between mean weight (in grams) and the sum of the differentials. [After D. S. Falconer, *Symposium on Genetics of Population Structure*, Publ. Internat. Union Biol. Sciences, Series B, no. 15, pp. 16–41, Naples, 1954.]

must, however, represent to some uncertain degree *genotypic selection*. In each generation Falconer selected the heavier mice at six weeks of age and let them interbreed. Correspondingly, mice of the lighter weight were selected and interbred. This artificial phenotypic selection resulted in different directions of adaptation: one population increased in weight, the other decreased. By twenty generations the response to selection was reduced. This could reflect an increase of genetic homozygosity in each line of selection. This is often a result of inbreeding. Alternatively, the reduction of response to selection could represent a depletion of additive genetic variation. And if this were truly the case, we might use it as a very rough example to illustrate nonmathematically R. A. Fisher's "fundamental theorem of natural selection" that states: "The rate of increase in fitness of any organism at any time is equal to its genetic variance in fitness at that time."

Falconer's interpretation of the experiments cited emphasizes, however, that natural selection among the mice populations studied can itself interact with the artificial selection applied by man. In Table 4·1 the expected and effective selection differentials are given for both the upward and downward selection experiments noted above. R denotes the response to selection. It is the difference between mean phenotype of the offspring of selected individuals of one generation and that

TABLE 4·1

Expected and Effective Selection Differential Values for Weight of Mice
Selected Upward and Downward

DIRECTION OF SELECTION	GENERATION NUMBERS	SELECTION DIFFERENTIAL PER GENERATION (GRAMS)		
		expected	effective	effective expected
Upward	1–22	1.39	1.36	0.98
	23–30	1.08	1.09	1.01
Downward	1–18	1.03	0.96	0.93
	19–24	0.82	0.70	0.86

Source: D. S. Falconer, *Introduction to Quantitative Genetics*, New York: The Ronald Press
Company, 1960.

of the whole preceding generation. The estimate of selection applied is
designated as S, the selection differential. It is the mean phenotype of
the parents selected as such in one generation expressed as the deviation
from the mean phenotype of the previous generation's parents. The
relation between response (R) and the selection differential (S) is
shown in Figure 4·6. An understanding of the manifold effects of
phenotypic selection is now necessary. In one phenotype many gene

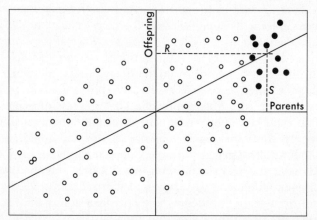

Figure 4·6. Relation of R (response to selection) to S (selection differential).
R is the difference between mean phenotype of the offspring of the *selected* parents
and the mean for the parental generation *in toto* before selection. S is the mean
phenotypic value of the individuals selected as parents taken as the deviation from
the mean phenotypic value of the parental generation *prior* to selection. Closed
circles denote selected parents and their offspring. The cross denotes their mean
phenotypic value, and the regression coefficient (see Chapter 3) of offspring on
parents is equal to R/S. [After D. S. Falconer, *Introduction to Quantitative Genetics*,
New York: The Ronald Press Company, 1960.]

complexes are linked together. Selection for one trait or character in the phenotype unavoidably selects for more than one gene or polygenic system. These unpredictable selections of genotype by selection of one phenotype character accumulate, and thus affect over several generations the nature of the response to selection.

In conclusion, Falconer was able to shift the population mean for body weight in mice from an original value near 22 grams to 14 for downward and 28 grams for the upward selection. The result in each case was genotypic response of the populations concerned to phenotypic selection. This is directional selection. These were heritable changes, for subsequent termination of selection on either group did not result in following generations to a return to the original condition of body weight of 22 grams.

Rapid Adaptation by Directional Selection

Although we rarely see the effects of natural selection, there are situations where rapid results of selection on populations can be observed or recorded. Selection is not always invisible or very slow. Rapid adaptation may occur when the arrays of selection pressures in operation on a population rapidly change in their qualitative as well as quantitative attributes, or when a population or the founders of a population are in some way introduced into a new environment. Three such examples are particularly instructive in showing the directional aspect of natural selection.

EVIDENCE FROM INDUSTRIAL MELANISM AND INTRODUCED SPECIES

INDUSTRIAL MELANISM. For the following beautiful example of adaptation we are indebted to the investigations, interpretations, and calculations of Kettlewell, Ford, and Haldane. A variety of species of *Lepidoptera* have in recent years become dark in their general coloration in industrial areas where the surrounding terrain and vegetation have been darkened by the pollution of smoke. Kettlewell in particular has made a careful study of one such species, *Biston betularia*. During the last one hundred years, in several urban regions of England, dark-colored or black (melanic) individuals of this and other species have occurred in increasing frequency in local populations. This is especially true for populations of *betularia* in the vicinity of industrial centers. For example, the first black specimen of *betularia* is reported to have occurred in Manchester in 1848. By 1895, approximately 98 per cent of the *betularia* population there was melanistic in appearance. Because the species has one generation per year, this example reveals a situation where within fifty generations a genotype of less than 1 per cent frequency shifted to a frequency of near 98 per cent.

Haldane has calculated that the darkening of the environment by smoke has increased the selective advantage of the dark-colored phenotype to 30 per cent over the light-colored phenotype. The magnitude of this change is far greater than can be expected from recurrent mutation. Since new melanistic individuals of this species occur infrequently in regions clean and unpolluted from smoke, mutation is evidently the source of the genotype of the dark-colored phenotype. It is not, however, the cause of the rise in population frequency of the phenotype. Dispersal of dark individuals from the "dirty" regions into "clean" ones does occur, but the weight of evidence is that there is a low rate of recurrent mutation for the genotype of the melanistic individual, and that selection seizes upon this mutation for increased fitness of local populations. The theory is that previously these dark-colored mutants were at a selective disadvantage on their light-colored background—namely, tree trunks and other lichen-covered vegetation. Then with increased pollution of local vegetation by industrial smoke, it is theorized that the dark-colored or black mutant gained superiority in fitness. In this way, respective gene frequencies were altered by natural selection. The genetic system controlling light-colored appearance decreased, and the genetic system operating for melanism increased.

It appears in this instance that the mutant for melanism is *dominant,* not *recessive,* to its allelic counterpart, and this may be one reason why the frequency of the mutant in the population has been altered so rapidly. Kettlewell has in fact shown that the rise in frequency of the mutant form in an industrial population is rapid and sigmoid in nature. Not surprisingly, the rise is rather similar to the demonstration in Chapter 3 (see Figure 3·4) of the greater ease with which selection can increase the frequency of a dominant in comparison to a recessive allele. But the question remains: through what channels of selection does nature in industrial regions favor the dark-colored or melanistic form of *Biston betularia?* This has been discovered by Kettlewell.

Biologists have long known that the colorations of animals often harmonize with that of their immediate environments. To cite only one case, rodents usually have their pelt colorations in harmony with the color of the soil or ground on which they live: light on light or dark on dark. This was nearly always explained as being caused by differential predation, which thus adapts the populations. If animals were protectively colored, they would be less subject to predation. So the theory stated that individual heritable variations which varied in the direction of the coloration of the environment would be at a selective advantage.

TABLE 4·2

**Differential Effects of Predation on the Peppered Moth
Biston betularia in England**

	TYPICAL	CARBONARIA	TOTAL
Nonindustrial area—1955			
(Dorset; vegetation not polluted			
by smoke)			
Released	496	473	969
Recaptured	62	30	92
Per cent recovery	12.5	6.3	9.5
Industrial area—1953			
(Birmingham; vegetation polluted)			
Released	137	447	584
Recaptured	18	123	141
Per cent recovery	13.1	27.5	24.1

Typical refers to light-colored forms, and *carbonaria* refers to the dark-colored form or mutant.
Source: H. B. D. Kettlewell, *Heredity*, 9:323–342; 10:287–301, 1956.

L. R. Dice and others have previously shown this on an experimental basis for external color of deermice (*Peromyscus maniculatus*) preyed upon by owls. And experiments with other animals have also shown the rather obvious selective advantage of protective coloration.

Kettlewell, working with released and captured individuals of either form of *betularia*, has examined and shown the selective advantage of such protective coloration on a sound statistical basis. We will simply abstract one part of his extensive investigation. From 1953 to 1955, he studied survival values for the two phenotypes of this species in, respectively, a nonindustrial and an industrial region of England. In each environmental situation he released a certain number of dark-colored and light-colored forms of *betularia*, recaptured them by light traps, and determined the frequency of the two forms among the recaptured. Some of his data (for male individuals only, since females are not normally caught by light traps) are summarized in Table 4·2. Ignoring the statistics of his findings (which are significant) as well as the immediate details of his experimental technique (which was well-controlled), we observe from his data that the light-colored phenotype has a higher survival value in the unpolluted regions than the dark-colored or melanistic phenotype. Kettlewell's findings point clearly to a selective advantage for dark-colored phenotypes in the polluted or industrial areas of England.

Direct observations on the nature of predation on dark- and light-colored forms placed on light- and dark-colored tree trunks have also

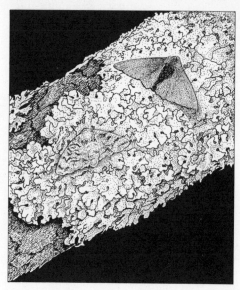

Figure 4·7. Typical (light-colored) and carbonaria (dark-colored) forms of *Biston betularia* on an unpolluted, lichen-covered tree. [After H. B. D. Kettlewell, *Heredity*, 10: 287–301, 1956.]

been made by Kettlewell. Birds were observed and photographed by him in the process of taking the conspicuous individuals from lichen-covered tree trunks. These facts are shown in Figures 4·7, 4·8, and 4·9. Conspicuousness of *betularia* (insofar as predation is concerned) is evidently controlled by (1) the phenotype of the individual *and* (2) the phenotype of its environment. In this way, Kettlewell has provided an adaptation model to explain the phenomenon of industrial melanism in *Lepidoptera*. Within fifty years, or fifty generations, a dominant mutant has been given a selective advantage by change in the population's environment. Thus natural selection, exercised primarily by birds prey-

Figure 4·8. Typical (light-colored) and carbonaria (dark-colored) forms of *Biston betularia* on blackened bark in a polluted region of England. [After H. B. D. Kettlewell, *Heredity*, 10: 287–301, 1956.]

ing upon conspicuous insect phenotypes, has operated on the less fit phenotype to shift the population in the direction: light-colored phenotype → dark-colored phenotype. Industrial melanism is a superb example of natural selection operating in a directional manner to increase the frequency of a phenotype and its correlated genotype within a population.

ECOGEOGRAPHICAL ADAPTATION IN THE HOUSE SPARROW. The house or English sparrow (*Passer domesticus*) was introduced into North America in 1852. Since then it has spread throughout nearly all of North and Middle America. It is a sedentary or nonmigratory species, and occurs generally in close proximity to urban, garden, or farm situations. Recently, R. K. Selander and R. F. Johnston have studied group variations in this species. They have compared mean values for various biological characters varying between the geographically distributed populations of this species. They find that most of the trends in geographical variations known for native American species are now exhibited by this species. Climatic or ecogeographical variation, and its implications for evidence of clinal intraspecific trends in population adaptation, is taken up later in this chapter, but here we are concerned with the rapidity of adaptation and evolution.

Figure 4·10 exemplifies Bergmann's rule for the North American populations of the house sparrow. The body weight of individuals in populations increases with the decrease in temperature and increase with (northern) latitude, as indexed by isophane values. These differential adaptations have occurred within one hundred generations of breeding of the house sparrow following its introduction into North America. All individuals of these populations are descended from a few individu-

Figure 4·9. An English robin, *Erithacus rubecula*, that has just taken a carbonaria form of *Biston betularia* off a tree trunk that is not blackened. [After a photograph taken by H. B. D. Kettlewell.]

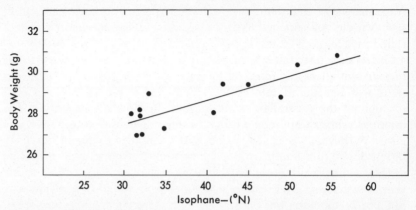

Figure 4·10. Correlation between severe winter temperature and mean body weight for fourteen populations of the house sparrow, *Passer domesticus,* in North America. The isophane values indicate severe winter climate (or decreased winter temperature). The graph shows the increase in individual size at higher latitudes and in colder environments for populations of this species. [After R. F. Johnston and R. K. Selander, *Science, 144:* 548–550, 1964.]

als introduced at the same time in the eastern United States. We see that not only has this species increased in numbers in North America, but that also gene frequencies have in all probability shifted rapidly in various populations as they dispersed in the diverse environments of North America. Selander and Johnston also found for this introduced species that characters such as color (Gloger's rule), tarsus length, and so on, vary with change in continental environment. They note that because the house sparrow has been in some parts of this continent only since 1900, many of those population adaptations must have occurred within fifty years or generations. Although the relative contributions of environment (phenotypic effects) and genotype (genotypic effects) to the observed, interpopulation variations in the characters of this species remain to be described, Selander and Johnston demonstrate rapid morphological changes in an introduced species. Thus they can infer in a convincing manner that evolution at the racial or subspecific level may be extremely rapid. This is one documentation of Darwin's prediction given in Chapter 1.

VIRUS RESISTANCE IN THE RABBIT. F. Fenner, W. R. Sobey, and others have described another example of extremely rapid adaptation or evolution in an introduced species. In 1859, twenty-four European rabbits (*Oryctolagus cuniculus*) were introduced into Australia. Six years later, in 1865, far more than twenty thousand individuals existed as a result of the initial population explosion. This increase in rabbit population, obviously unchecked by limiting factors, continued until nearly all of Australia was populated. By 1950, the rabbit population of

Australia was of an order of several hundred million. There is in Central and Middle America a virus (*Myxoma*) which produces a disease called myxomatosis in the rabbit. This virus results in skin lesions and an infectious state, followed by death. Insects are the vector of transmission, with fleas and mosquitoes being the primary ones. In 1950 this virus was introduced into Australia. By 1954 the virus had spread throughout the Australian populations of rabbit. In one locality, one hundred rabbits were inoculated with a virulent, Brazilian type of the virus. Within six weeks after the first appearance of natural cases, the rabbit population dropped from five thousand to fifty. The death rate in this locality was later calculated to be 99.8 per cent. The following year it was found that in previously uninfected rabbits, the mortality induced by the virus was only 90 per cent.

Three possibilities were then considered: (1) change in host resistance; (2) change in virus virulence; and (3) an environmental factor influencing host response to virus. Each possibility seems to be in operation here, and since 1954 deaths attributable to the virus have decreased further, to about 5 per cent. This is a result of the genetic adaptation of both the virus *and* of its host, the rabbit. With such originally high mortality values (99.8 per cent), it is not difficult to see the vacancies available in the Australian habitats for rabbit offspring (and their offspring in turn) of any genetic variant with the slightest resistance to the virus. Reciprocally, there is excellent evidence that the virus itself has lost part of its virulence. Although application of the principle in this instance is uncertain, students should remember that a host-specific parasite that destroys its host directly selects against itself. The parasite or infectious species which does not kill a host or prevent it from breeding, however, has a selective advantage over its counterpart which does! This is an example of directional genetic adaptation of populations of rabbit stemming from virus invasion and colonization. A rapid adaptation occurred when the rabbit's physiological environment was altered by an introduced virus species. High death rates at first, followed by slightly lower rates, permitted a situation for genetic selection of virus-resistant individuals in the rabbit. This type of adaptation—should we say evolution?—took place within ten years!

Trends in Adaptation

Prior to discussing two trends or patterns in adaptation at the intraspecific level, it is of value to think of the multifactorial basis of adaptation. Evolutionists consider the adaptation of an organism or a population to its environment to be a resultant or compromise between several selection forces. Thus, the adaptation of a population to its local environment reflects a net selection pressure which has interacting components of several selection forces. By the multifactorial concept of adaptation, there is no simple solution to the problem of adaptation of a population. An adaptation is considered to be an *ad hoc* response of the population to the net selection pressure operating on it at any one period of time. A variety of selection forces may contribute to this net selection pressure. One warning is necessary here. Because the adjustment in genotypes of a population to selection pressure is in fact a response, and because the environment of a population is as a rule varying, then we should expect to observe for a population studied the results of selection pressure that were in operation during the previous generation(s). We may visualize a lag between the operation of selection and the associated response of the genotype-phenotype complex of the population. It is difficult to find better statements of the ideas alluded to here than those of E. Mayr (1960, p. 495) and R. C. Lewontin (1965; p. 304). Mayr writes: "Adaptation is a temporary balance between the numerous demands made on an organism by the environment, or, to express it in terms of modern evolutionism, it is a compromise between many selection pressures, some occasionally quite antagonistic to each other." Lewontin has written: ". . . genetic changes take place to increase the fitness of the population in *today's* environment but the result of that change is a population in the next generation living in *tomorrow's* environment."

ECOGEOGRAPHIC VARIATION AND REGULATION OF CLUTCH SIZE IN BIRDS

Ecogeographic Variation.   Description and interpretation of regular or nonrandom trends in the variations of organisms at the intraspecific level played an important role during the 1940's and 1950's in the return by biologists to a Darwinian position in considering the various populations of a species to be adapted to their respective environment. Knowledge of such correlated variations in organism and environment has done much to strengthen the idea that evolution is the summation of microevolutionary changes. Julian Huxley proposed the term *cline* to describe the empirical observation of a correlation between a character gradient and a gradient in the environment. We have seen that body weight or size in the house sparrow is positively correlated with latitude, and thus negatively correlated with winter temperature. This is an example of Bergmann's rule which states that for warm-blooded or homeothermic organisms, body size is inversely associated with temperature. Figure 4·11 illustrates this for the Western European populations of the great tit (*Parus major*). This species and the house sparrow are sedentary or at least nonmigratory organisms. In Figure 4·12 we see that a migratory bird species, previously thought to dis-

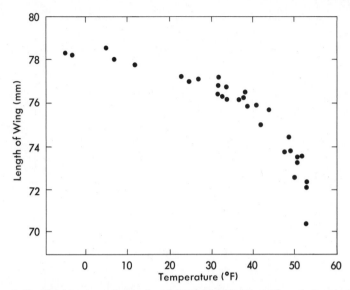

Figure 4·11. The inverse relation between wing length and mean temperature of the coldest month of the year for thirty-one populations of the great tit, *Parus major*, in Western and Central Europe. [From D. W. Snow, *Evolution, 8:* 19–28, 1954.]

obey Bergmann's rule, does in fact exemplify the rule when the temperatures of its populations' winter quarters are compared to wing length, which is an index to body size. The overriding importance of winter temperature, or severe seasonal climate, should be obvious here. Bernard Rensch has surveyed the European passerine avifauna for manifestations of Bergmann's rule, and finds that about 84 per cent obey the rule. The parallelism in response to environment of many animal species is most striking.

A variety of ecogeographical or climatic rules could be cited. These are well worked out for avian and mammalian species, and examples are also known for cold-blooded or poikilothermal species. For example, fish populations in cold waters have more vertebral segments than their counterparts in warmer waters. Among birds and mammals, other classic rules are those of *Gloger* (increased pigment deposition, and thus darker hue or color, in humid regions compared to arid regions) and of *Allen* (decreased appendage length in cold regions). Evolutionists studying such phenomena now consider that clines frequently represent compromises between several selection forces. These forces vary in the environment of species where populations vary in characters such as wing length, body size, ear length, tarsus length, plumage or pelt color, and others. Many trends in variations previously thought to be exceptions or departures from the rules can thus be explained.

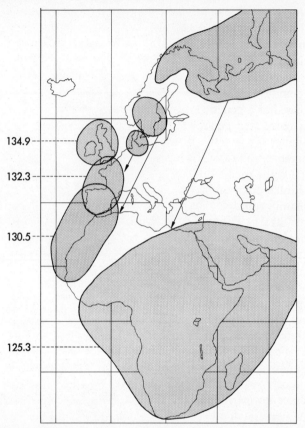

Figure 4·12. Leap-frog migration and variation in wing length in the plover, *Charadrius hiaticula*, in Western Europe and Africa. Winter ranges are denoted by arrows. Note that a comparison of wing length on the basis of winter distributions shows increased wing length in colder regions, hinting of Bergmann's rule. [After F. Salomonsen, *Dan. Biol. Medd.*, 22: 1–62, 1955.]

The study of ecogeographical variation divides into two separate studies: one involves empirical description of clines; the other is concerned with interpretations of their adaptive significance (which really means guessing at the nature of the agents acting on the populations exhibiting the cline). We will mostly avoid this controversial topic, and consider only the accepted explanation for the adaptive significance of Bergmann's rule. This states that increased body size in cold regions is an adaptation for heat economy. The theory here is that with increase in volume, there is a corresponding decrease in the surface area-to-volume ratio, and thus minimum loss of heat to the environment. Whether this is true or not is uncertain, but recent experimental work supports the point. Biologists have long known that homeothermic organisms raised in warm conditions over several generations become smaller in size than individuals reared in cooler temperatures. S. A. Barnett has studied the effects of cold temperature on rodents raised at low temperatures for many generations. He finds that such experimentals demonstrate increased body size after several generations. This increase has a genetic basis, and is not merely a shift in phenotype without a correlated genotypic shift. Other experimental studies provided evidence for genetic shifts to smaller size at warm temperatures. Taken together, the experimental studies of Barnett and G. A. Harrison, as well as the earlier ones of H. Przibram provide good evidence for the classic interpretation that heat economy is one adaptive significance for Bergmann's rule.

CLUTCH SIZE IN PASSERINE BIRD SPECIES. If we accept the premise that natural selection operates for the evolution of increased reproductive capacity, then we may wonder why elephants don't produce more young more rapidly than they do! Students unfamiliar with the multifactorial basis of adaptation and the fact that the phenotype is a compromise of various selection forces or pressures often fall into this conceptual trap. Data now available for seasonal and geographic variation in clutch size within bird species provide one answer. For such data and its careful interpretation, we are indebted to David Lack and his co-workers at the Edward Grey Institute at Oxford. Incidentally, students should compare the following discussion with the preceding one concerned with regulation of population size in Chapter 3. The two—one theoretical, one empirical with interpretations being deduced —supplement each other. Lack has demonstrated that clutch size in many birds is often regulated by natural selection to produce the maximum number of offspring that can successfully achieve independence from the family environment, and thus enter the local environment as potential breeding individuals. Parental care and attention to offspring are most important factors here.

Lack notes that for birds and mammals a limit is set on family size (litter or clutch size) by the sharing of food among the offspring. Thus if there are too many offspring in a single brood, fewer rather than more young survive to breed in the following generation(s). There appears to be a limit on family size set by availability of food. In other animals, particularly the less advanced organisms without parental care, more young are produced, and there is correspondingly a greater mortality for those young. Here the egg-laying capacity is limited by the physiological capacity of the adult, and there is a general trend for either a few large eggs or many small eggs to be laid.

In Figure 4·13 we see geographical variation in clutch size for the

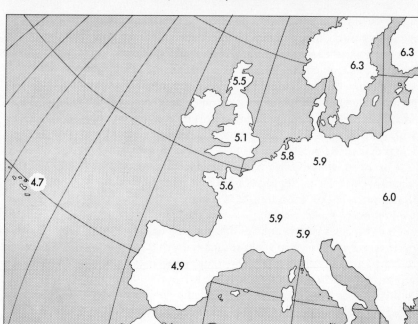

Figure 4·13. Latitudinal variation in average clutch size in the European robin, *Erithacus rubecula*. [After D. Lack, *The Natural Regulation of Animal Numbers*, Oxford: Oxford University Press, 1954.]

European robin (*Erithacus rubecula*). Note that clutch size increases as latitude rises. Lack explains this by stating that birds breeding at higher latitudes have a longer day for the feeding and care of young than their equivalents at lower latitudes. Thus they can effectively raise to the adult state a larger number of offspring. For example, the summer day in Central Europe is about fifty per cent longer than that at the equator. Lack argues that this is an explanation of clinal variation in clutch size in bird species. The majority of diurnal bird and mammal species seem to show this latitudinal increase in clutch or litter size. Whether nocturnal birds and mammals truly show this latitudinal trend is unknown, but if it is subsequently shown that they do not (or do to a lesser degree), this will be a major confirmation of Lack's theory. At any one latitudinal position, following Lack's argument as well as his findings in England, clutch sizes of birds are expected to vary from year to year depending upon the severity of climate and availability of food. It is believed that selection adapts local populations to produce the maximum number of young that can successfully become independent breeding members of next year's population. The Oxford school of ecologists under Lack has most adequately documented this for local populations of members of the tit genus *Parus*. Their findings demonstrate convincingly that the clutch size of these birds which feed their young in the nest has evolved to that number which on an average produces most young to survive and contribute offspring to the next generation. The majority of offspring of tits in any one breeding season are victims of mortality by the following winter. Competition for food and severe climate are limiting factors here, and it is clear that natural selection works for an optimum clutch size by operating on individuals according to the numbers of offspring they leave. Neither small nor large numbers are optimum.

Adaptation in clutch size in birds is best interpreted as a compromise of selection forces in operation on local populations. Birds produce average numbers of young which are neither too small nor too large. With too few offspring decreased fitness of genotypes results and selection will rapidly increase the rate of reproduction; with too many offspring decreased fitness results from diminution of the food supply available to the young. Limitation of food in the habitat, and a limit of food that the parents can provide the young, are the important considerations when there are too many offspring. In Figure 4·14, we see for the great tit (*Parus major*) the positive relation between average clutch size and abundance of food in its habitat. Clutch size is truly a compromise of various selective forces. For a population at a given locality, or for com-

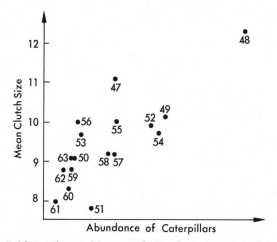

Figure 4·14. Evidence for positive correlation between annual average clutch size and abundance of caterpillars for the population of the great tit, *Parus major*, in Marley Wood, near Oxford, England, from 1947 to 1961. [From C. M. Perrins, *J. Animal Ecology*, **34:** 601–647, 1965.]

parison of populations at different localities, environmental differences, coupled with the reproductive nature of the parental birds themselves, determine an optimum number of young that can successfully be raised for maximal contribution of offspring—that is, genes—to the next generation.

M. L. Cody, following the *principle of allocation* developed by R. Levins and R. H. MacArthur, has recently analyzed ecogeographic trends in variation in clutch size in a manner which subsumes but does not preclude previous hypotheses such as those presented above. Cody emphasizes that organisms have a limited amount of time or energy, and that natural selection will operate for allocations of time or energy in a manner which maximizes the contribution of a genotype to following generations during the adaptation of the phenotype. He notes that in unstable environments populations are usually maintained at densities below the carrying capacity $(\overline{K})$, and that here natural selection proceeds to maximize the reproductive rate r (see Chapter 3). He reasons that in stable environments population will be maintained at the level of $\overline{K}$, or that $\overline{K}$ will be increased by selection. In this instance, following the principle of allocation, energy will be conserved by reducing r. Uses to which this conserved energy might be put are avoidance of predation, competition with other species (see Chapters 5 and 6), or enlargement of clutch size. Cody visualizes by a three-dimensional graph (Figure 4·15A) that these three requirements or energy drains interact in ways which can be used to predict the particular allocations of energy by various phenotypes. In this manner, the reported trends of variations in clutch size from temperate to tropical latitudes for some open-nesting birds, predation-free birds, and hole-nesting birds on continents and for island-nesting birds are predicted by his model (Figure 4·15B). There is not space here to present the observed data his model predicts, but it is sufficient to state that it predicts the increased clutch sizes of bird species that ornithologists and ecologists have noted in the higher continental latitudes and in elevations of mountains (unstable environments), as well as the reduced clutch sizes that occur in the tropics, on islands, and at lower elevations of mountains (more stable environments). Cody's analysis suggests that in temperate zones most energy is used to increase the reproductive rate r and thus the clutch size, whereas the carrying capacity $(\overline{K})$ is more important in the tropics, with an attendant reduction in r. In other words, in the unstable environment the selective advantage for individuals centers around the quantity of young produced, whereas in the stable environment quantity is less advantageous. We may guess that here (for example, birds in the tropical lowland forests) natural selection in increasing fitness operates for quality rather than quantity in the offspring produced (see Figure 6·2).

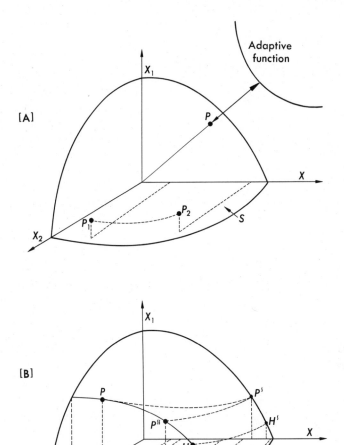

Figure 4·15. Three-dimension graphs showing point or points of intersection (P) of the surface of phenotypes (S) with an adaptive function. The phenotype P receives benefits proportional to its intercepts on the axis X, X_1, and X_2, resulting from the division of energy between clutch size, avoidance of predation, and competing ability, respectively. **A:** The model. **B:** Application of the model for variation (broken lines) in the path of the adaptive function from temperate to tropical latitudes for continental species (P'–P, open-nesting birds; P'–P'', predation-free birds; H'–H, hole-nesting birds) and island-nesting species (Q–Q'). For the complete explanation of this model **(A)** and its application **(B)**, the student should consult Cody's paper cited below. An *equilibrium approach* to the study of ecology and adaptation is again demonstrated. Of particular interest here is that multifactorial analysis has been used to predict ecogeographic variation in a manner similar to the prediction of insular variation in species abundance (see Figure 3·17). [After M. L. Cody, *Evolution*: 174–184, 1966.]

Conclusion

In this chapter we have examined the vector nature of selection pressures in operation on a population. These are described as centripetal or stabilizing, directional, or disruptive in nature. Examples of adaptation are considered for rapid directional selection in introduced species or in species when the native environment changes abruptly. With several exceptions that involve shifts in individual variations within a population, most of the examples of adaptation taken up in this chapter are inferred or deduced from empirical cases of group variations at the intraspecific level. We have noted that the adaptation of a population is a two-step process: operation of natural selection → population response. Thus we realize that selection *results* in differential reproduction, and it should be clear to the student that there are alternative pathways to differential reproduction and associated increases in fitness of individuals and populations. Finally, in our consideration of the relation of selection to adaptation we are now assuming that adaptation is usually multifactorial, and rarely the result of a single selection force or pressure.

Further Reading

Baker, H. G., and G. Ledyard Stebbins, Eds. *The Genetics of Colonizing Species.* New York: Academic Press, 1965.

Cody, M. L. "A General Theory of Clutch Size." *Evolution, 20:* 174–184, 1965.

Ford, E. B. *Ecological Genetics.* London: Methuen and Co., Ltd., 1964.

Grant, V. *The Origin of Adaptations.* New York: Columbia University Press, 1963.

Hamilton, T. H. "The Adaptive Significance of Intraspecific Trends of Variation in Wing Length and Body Size Among Bird Species." *Evolution, 15:* 180–195, 1961.

Lack, D. *The Natural Regulation of Animal Numbers.* London: Oxford University Press, 1954.

Lewontin, R. C. "Selection in and of Populations." Pp. 297–312, in *Ideas in Modern Biology.* Garden City (New York): The Natural History Press, 1965.

Mather, K. "The Genetical Structure of Populations." *Symposia of the Society for Experimental Biology, 7:* 66–95, 1953.

Mayr, E. *Animal Species and Evolution.* Cambridge, Mass.: Harvard University Press, 1963.

————. "Chairman's Introduction to the Symposium on Adaptive Evolution." *Proceedings of the XIIth International Ornithological Congress, Helsinki,* pp. 495–498, 1960.

Sheppard, P. M. *Natural Selection and Heredity.* London: Hutchinson and Co., Ltd., 1958.

Simpson, G. G. *The Major Features of Evolution.* New York: Columbia University Press, 1953.

Thoday, J. M. "Components of Fitness." *Symposia of the Society for Experimental Biology, 7 :* 96–113, 1953.

The Origins of Species and Species Differences

The genes within a gene pool form a harmonious whole which can evolve only as a whole. The first step, then, in the multiplication of species, is a physical separation of a portion of the species, permitting it to go its own way genetically. What happens after this isolation depends on the genetic contents of the isolated population, on the totality of selection forces working on it and on numerous chance phenomena (mutation, recombination, etc.).

MAYR, 1959, p. 226.

THE STUDY OF EVOLUTION is the study of population adaptation and of species differences. For an appreciation of the latter topic an awareness of the requirements for speciation—for the multiplication of species—is necessary. This topic is developed in the present chapter, and continued in the following or last chapter where the species, following Mayr's thinking, is considered the keystone of evolution. Mayr has devoted a lifetime to the study of speciation in animal species. We will rely to a large extent on his conclusions, but will not disregard the notable work of others. Both the origin of species and species differences will be examined.

A species may be envisioned as an isolated pool of genes flowing through space and time, constantly adapting to changes in its environment as well as to the new environments encountered by its extension into other geographic regions. At various intervals of time and in different environments, portions of this gene pool may become isolated. Such isolates may (1) become extinct, (2) reunite with the parental species, or (3) differentiate during isolation to form new species which in turn pass through space and time. Before considering the immediate problem of origin of isolates, races, and species, let us examine some general characteristics of animal species.

1. Each species is an isolated pool of genes possessing regional (racial, populational) characteristics in gene complexes which are interconnected by gene flow.
2. Each species fills an ecological niche *not exactly* utilized by another species.
3. Each species is in process of continually adjusting to its environment.
4. Each species possesses a constellation of isolating mechanisms that indirectly or directly prevent exchange of genes with related species.
5. Each species has the capacity to give rise to new species provided some form of geographic or spatial isolation gives its isolates an opportunity to develop a unique gene pool without being swamped by gene flow from the parental species.

Geographic Isolation as a Prerequisite for Speciation

Geographic isolation is one aspect of species multiplication which Darwin and Wallace failed to understand completely. Its theoretical development starts with the early studies of M. Wagner, H. Seebohm, K. Jordan, and E. B. Poulton and passes through the subsequent work of Rensch, Dobzhansky, Huxley, Stebbins, and Ford to its recent culmination by Mayr in his *Animal Species and Evolution*. The following sequence in speciation is now universally accepted for sexually reproducing animal species; species $\longrightarrow\!\!\!\!\!\!\!\backslash$ $\longmapsto$ isolated population → isolate → race or incipient species → species. The waved line between species and isolated populations represents an extrinsic barrier restricting or stopping gene flow between the isolated population and its parental species. This allopatric isolation is the primary step in the origin of new animal species. Figure 5·1 illustrates in a hypothetical manner such a mode of speciation. It further provides a dimension of time with which to compare the origin of new species in relation to their passage or flow through space and time.

The importance of *spatial* or *geographic* isolation in the origin of races and species is particularly obvious when we examine the distribution of related populations, races, or species on islands off continents or in isolated archipelagos where there is opportunity for species multiplication between islands. We will see an example of the latter in Chapter 6, in a discussion of the phenomenon of adaptive radiation. In Figure 5·2 the distributions of races or isolates are shown for the Papuan kingfisher (*Tanysiptera hydrocharis-galatea*) on New Guinea and its smaller offshore or neighboring islands. On New Guinea three

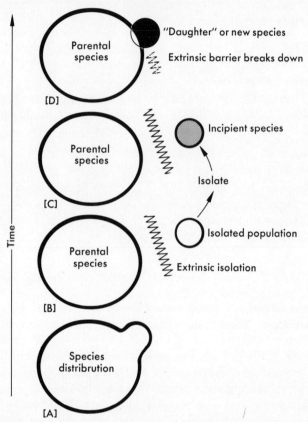

Figure 5·1. Some stages in the process of allopatric speciation. Stages **A–D** represent isolation of a population by extrinsic or geographic isolation. The isolate undergoes genetic differentiation to a point where it remains effectively reproductively isolated from the parental species, when the extrinsic barrier breaks down (or is overcome) and individuals of the two (by now) separate genetic systems come in contact.

races occur, each on a separate distributional island. These are the beginnings of new species. We call them, in different contexts, *incipient species, races, subspecies,* or *isolates.* This example shows that isolation is correlated with increased differences in the biological characteristics of the isolates observed. Such differences or adaptations culminate and are reflected in taxonomic distinction. Many similar examples could be cited for animal species. The North and Middle American distributions of members of the mouse superspecies *Peromyscus maniculatus* are shown in Figure 5·3. The increase in numbers of incipient species in the mountainous regions of Western America is obvious. From these data W. F. Blair concludes that wide distribution of species is favorable to speciation because of increased opportunities of isolation by extrinsic or environmental factors. In Figure 5·4 we see the distributions of the various races of the song sparrow (*Melospiza melodia*) in North and Middle America. Note that here increased subspeciation or differentiation of sections of the species occurs in western North America and Middle America where topographic diversity (effected by mountain ranges isolated by deserts and other distinctive physiographic features) enforces isolation. Isolation in this manner has permitted local populations to adapt to their respective environments with restriction of gene flow and associated genetic swamping from adjacent populations or races.

Gene flow should now be put in its proper perspective. We have considered it in Chapters 2 and 3 on a more theoretical or quantitative basis. Students of race formation, speciation, and morphological adaptation in isolates have found that gene flow is a conservative agent. That is, it holds down the tendency of populations to adapt to their local environments. In this sense, gene flow is considered a cohesive factor in a species and operates to counter weakly the effects of selection. To a certain moderate degree, gene flow keeps adjacent populations similar to each other.

Mayr in particular has emphasized the retarding role in adaptation of gene flow. He emphasizes the importance of the absence of genetic swamping by gene flow in the process of differentiation of isolates. The case of the Papuan kingfisher is a good example, showing that populations on the mainland or on a large island are exposed to a certain environment. Across a small water-gap from such land masses may occur an island the biotic and physical environment of which is essentially the same as the former. Yet in many such instances the population on the

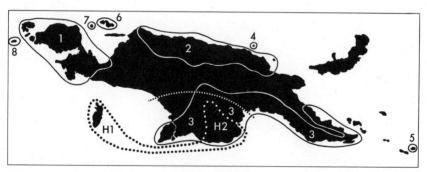

Figure 5·2. Distribution of the Papuan kingfishers (1–7) of the *Tanysiptera hydrocharis-galatea* group on New Guinea and the neighboring islands.
[Source: E. Mayr, "Change of Genetic Environment and Evolution," in J. Huxley, A. C. Hardy, and E. B. Ford (eds.), *Evolution as a Process*, London: George Allen and Unwin, Ltd., 1954.]

island, derived from populations in the former areas, will exhibit biological differences indicating a different or more complete adaptation to the same environment! Absence of gene flow and genetic swamping in population or isolate divergence, and the presence of these factors in the retardation of population divergence on continents are two sides of the speciation coin for continental and island environments.

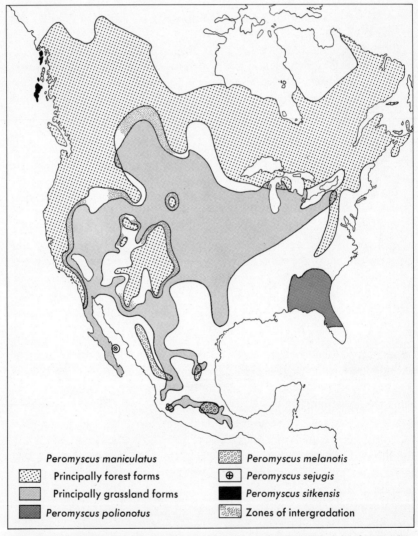

	Peromyscus maniculatus		Peromyscus melanotis
	Principally forest forms	⊕	Peromyscus sejugis
	Principally grassland forms		Peromyscus sitkensis
	Peromyscus polionotus		Zones of intergradation

Figure 5·3. Distribution of the five species (or incipient species) in the species group (or superspecies) of *Peromyscus maniculatus*. [After W. F. Blair, *Evolution*, 4: 253–274, 1950.]

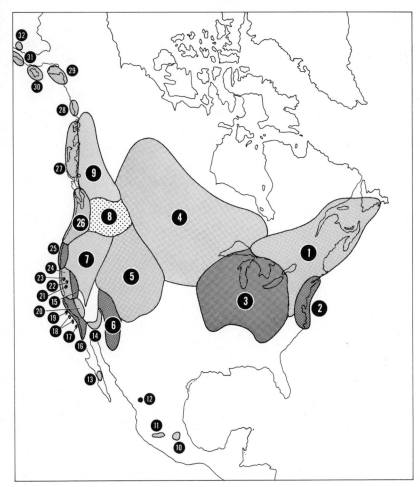

Figure 5·4. Distribution of subspecies of the song sparrow, *Melospiza melodia*, in North and Middle America. [After A. H. Miller, *Evolution*, 10: 262–277, 1956.]

ISOLATING MECHANISMS

FUNCTIONS AND CAUSES.   How are the gaps between related species maintained? We have seen that species are gene pools effectively isolated from one another. At least for animal species, spatial or geographic isolation is the usual prerequisite for speciation. But processes in nature are rarely complete and clear-cut from the viewpoint of the biologist or evolutionist. We will disregard here many of the factors responsible for geographic isolation. Suffice it to say, dispersal of a few individuals across a water-gap or desert, a natural catastrophe resulting in a new island off a peninsula, or the volcanic formation of a mountain

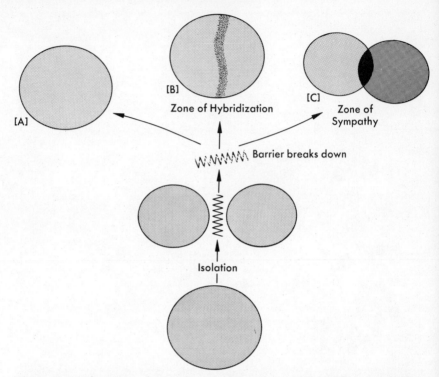

Figure 5·5. Alternative fates of an isolate whose individuals (secondarily) come into contact with those of the parental body of populations. A: Complete union of the two bodies of populations, showing absence of genetic differentiation in the isolate. **B:** Hybridization of individuals of the two bodies, showing only partial acquisition of isolating mechanisms by the isolate. **C:** Individuals of the paternal species and the isolate fail to interbreed and exchange genes upon interindividual contact. Thus reproductive isolation has occurred in the isolate, and it is now a good species.

are typical means whereby populations are isolated on continents, where habitats and common environments are extensive and far-reaching. In addition, fluctuations of species ranges on continents over many generations may leave isolates on the periphery of the species' ranges. The net result, however, is that a population is *peripherally isolated* from the main body of the species' populations. Figure 5·5 illustrates the alternative fates that may await such an isolate. Because an isolate may achieve different levels of divergence or biological difference from its parental species, we must consider (1) what causes the gaps between species and (2) what strengthens or reinforces the gaps between species.

THE ORIGIN OF GAPS BETWEEN SPECIES

THE ORIGIN OF GENETIC ISOLATING MECHANISMS. The gaps between species reflect the operation of isolating mechanisms. We will consider only intrinsic isolation mechanisms, which are the products of natural selection, and thus are adaptations. How do they arise, and how do they function? Many silly discussions have occurred concerning the functions and causes of isolating mechanisms. An explanation widely held some years ago had it that in isolation, certain differences developed between the isolate and its parental species. That is, an adaptation occurred in the isolate that did not occur in the parental species. When the isolate and the parental species came into contact— either by breakdown of the extrinsic barrier or by extension of either the parental species or the isolate's breeding range—the two forms were sufficiently different in genetics, behavior, and ecology that they did not interbreed. Thus a gap between two species was manifested. Not all contacts between isolates and parental species are this simple (see the problem of hybridization illustrated in Figure 5·6).

The weight of recent evidence, according to Mayr, suggests that "the greatest part of the genetic basis of the isolating mechanism is an incidental by-product of the genetic divergence of isolated gene pools and acquired during this isolation." This conclusion is in accordance with the theory that isolation is a prerequisite for speciation. Some evolutionists disagree with Mayr's conclusion, but their argument is usually that he should have said "the major part" rather than "the greatest part." There is evidence of reinforcement of isolating mechanisms in zones of sympatry between new species and their parental or related forms. Perhaps it is best to think of basic isolating mechanisms as being acquired by an isolate while it is in isolation or allopatry, and of auxiliary or modifying isolating mechanisms as being acquired in sympatry. In this situation, isolating mechanisms may be reinforced by interspecific selection pressures.

In any event, there is abundant support in the literature of animal systematics for the idea that basic isolating mechanisms are not produced in interspecific contact, but rather originate in isolation. In most cases of hybridization between bird species (see Figure 5·6) or of character displacement (see Figure 5·7) between two species, there is little or no evidence for the back-flow or spread of characters or adaptations acquired in the zones of overlap or contact. It is believed that in these cases swamping by gene flow from populations of either one of the interacting species (away from their zone of contact) work against such back-flow of characters. In Chapter 6 we will note again this problem for the exceptional situation of two species occurring on a small island. Here two species exhibiting some hybridization and/or competition will have coextensive distributions and the characters resulting from hybridization or displacement have the opportunity to become species specific.

In conclusion, isolating mechanisms are adaptations which indirectly

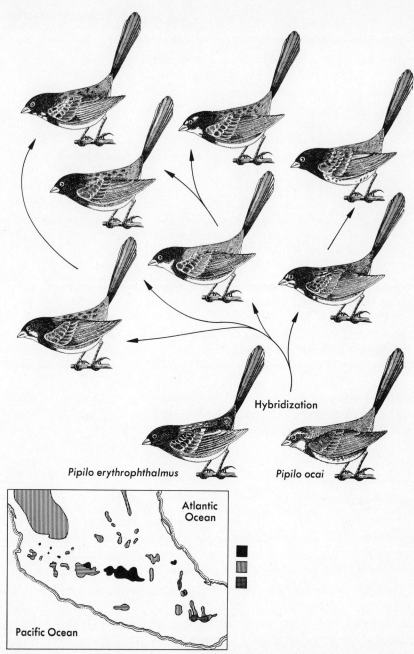

Pipilo erythrophthalmus

Hybridization

Pipilo ocai

Atlantic
Ocean

Pacific Ocean

Figure 5·6. Hybridization of two species of towhee (*Pipilo erythrophthalmus* and *P. ocai*) in Central Mexico. This is interpreted as a result of secondary contact (caused by man's disturbance of their previous separate habitats) and of incomplete differentiation of their respective genetics systems during previous isolation. The arrows indicate the various hybrid forms that have been described, and are not meant to indicate the sequences of their derivation. [After G. Sibley, *Evolution, 8:* 255–268, 1954.]

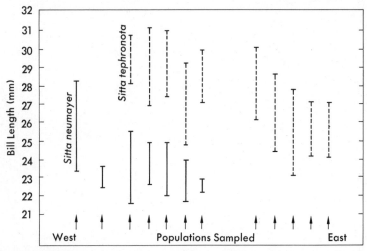

Figure 5·7. Character displacement in bill length for two species of nuthatch (*Sitta neumayer* and *S. tephronota*) in Asiatic regions adjacent to the Eastern Mediterranean. [After C. Vaurie, Am. Mus. Novitates, 1472: 681–689, 1950.]

or directly prevent the exchange of genes between species. They may be genetic and physiological (sterility factors), behavioral, or ecological in nature. The examples we have discussed lead to the topic of interspecific interactions. This is another aspect of natural selection. (Remember: individuals of other species as well as of the same species are all part of the environment of a given individual.)

Interspecific Interactions

Once again Darwin provides us with an excellent lead into our topic:

As the species of the same genus usually have, though by no means invariably, much similarity in habits and constitution, and always in structure, the struggle will generally be more severe between them, if they come into competition with each other, than between species of distinct genera.

DARWIN, 1859, p. 59.

Here we are concerned with populations where adaptation is in part a response to selection pressures stemming from negative density-dependent situations. This is adaptive adjustment of one species to the presence of another species. Two types of such adaptations can be discerned: one concerns ecological adjustments of populations of related species to a common environment; the other deals with behavioral responses of noninterbreeding, but behaviorally communicating individuals of interacting species.

AVOIDANCE OF ECOLOGICAL COMPETITION

GAUSE'S RULE, CHARACTER DISPLACEMENT, AND SELECTION FOR AVOIDANCE OF ECOLOGICAL COMPETITION. In recent years, David Lack and Robert MacArthur, as evolutionary ecologists primarily studying bird species, have been pre-eminent in advancing the thesis that ecological divergence of sympatric species is a consequence of Gause's rule. This states that two species cannot live the same way in the same place at the same time. But by varying the ways the species compete for resources in limited supply at a given point in the environment, the rule goes, natural selection permits two or more species to seemingly coexist within that environment. Table 5·1 summarizes Lack's findings for the ecological differences of sympatric passerine bird species in the British Isles, and Figure 5·8 illustrates MacArthur's findings of subtle species differences in his analysis of the ecological characteristics of five species of American wood warblers (*Dendroica* sp., *Parulidae*) in the northeastern United States. The two studies—one qualitative, one quantitative—illustrate Gause's rule. Nearly all cases of sympatric species living together in the same three-dimensional unit of the environment show, on more detailed analysis, differences in the ways the competing species divide up the environmental resources. Numerous examples for species of birds, mammals, amphibians and reptiles, and insects could be cited to illustrate Gause's rule. Much of contemporary ecology is simply an effort to document this rule on a more mathematical basis, and to take the results and use them to predict abundance of species and individuals, or the observed differences between species occurring in sympatry. Two examples of this point may be instructive.

CHARACTER DISPLACEMENT. D. Lack, C. Vaurie, E. O. Wilson, and W. L. Brown, Jr., have emphasized that when related species come into competition in small zones of overlap or sympatry, reciprocal inter-

TABLE 5·1
Ecological Isolation Among Some Congeneric British Passerine Bird Species

MEANS OF ECOLOGICAL ISOLATION	NUMBER OF CASES
Geographical differences	3
Habitat differences	18
Differences in foraging zone within the same habitat	3
Differences in food habits	1

Each case represents examination of ecological and distribution relations of two to several species of the same genus—that is, species sympatric in the British Isles.

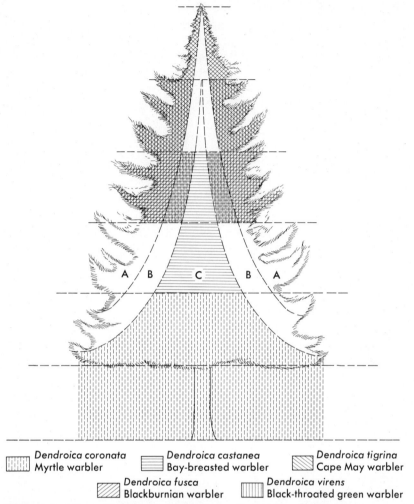

Dendroica coronata
Myrtle warbler

Dendroica castanea
Bay-breasted warbler

Dendroica tigrina
Cape May warbler

Dendroica fusca
Blackburnian warbler

Dendroica virens
Black-throated green warbler

Figure 5·8. Schematic diagram of differences in foraging frequencies in several zones of the spruce tree for five species of North American wood warblers (genus *Dendroica, Parulidae*). Although each species feeds in all zones, there are zone differences with respect to which each species utilizes at least one half of its foraging time. [After R. H. MacArthur, *Ecology, 39*: 599–619.]

specific selection pressures will intensify pre-existing differences, in order to minimize ecological competition. An example of this process is illustrated in Figure 5·7. The example involves intensification of differences in the feeding apparatus of two species of nuthatch (*Sitta neumayer* and *Sitta tephronota*) in Iran. In their zone of overlap only, the respective populations diverge in bill length and other biological characters. It is hypothesized that reciprocal selection pressures for avoidance of interspecific competition have operated to produce this character displacement. Comparable examples for other species of animals are now known, and they all reflect the validity of Gause's rule. An obvious approach to the study of character displacement is to express comparable measurements of the feeding apparatus of sympatric species as a ratio of the size of the smaller species to that of the larger species. G. E. Hutchinson and T. Schoener have utilized this approach in some detail. They find varying ratios for different kinds of sympatric species, and there is some evidence that tropical species when sympatric are less different (ratio: ≈ 1.0) than temperate or arctic pairs of sympatric species (ratio: >1.0). Whether this means greater niche overlap (hence reduced competition) among sympatric species in the tropics is uncertain, but this type of analysis is an indication of how ecologists are now studying interspecific interactions in nature.

COMMUNITY EVIDENCE FOR GAUSE'S RULE. Gause's rule for interspecific interactions in ecology has been confirmed in a variety of ways:

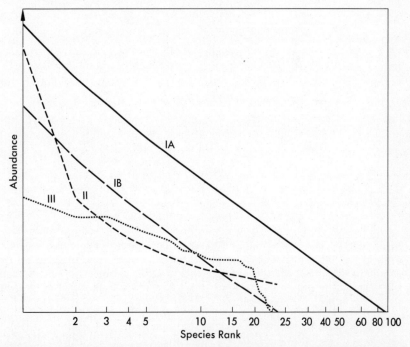

Figure 5·9. Some evidence that ecological niches are nonoverlapping and Gausian in distribution. The abundance of species when ranked from commonest to rarest is predicted by three models: *I*, Gausian, nonoverlapping niches; *II*, overlapping niches; *III*, noncontinuous, particular niches. *IA* is calculated for 105 bird species; *IB, II*, and *III* for 25 species. Model *I* gives the best prediction of the abundance data for consideration of either 105 or 25 species. [For the mathematical and statistical data, and further interpretation, the student is referred to R. H. MacArthur, *Proc. U.S. Nat. Acad. Sci.*, 43: 293–295, 1957, and his subsequent papers.]

by inductive experiments with organisms in the laboratory, and by deductive studies of natural conditions such as those noted above. Recently, another test has come from the study of the relative abundance of species. MacArthur has proposed three models to explain relative abundance of species at a given locality: (I) a Gausian model with nonoverlapping niches, (II) a nonGausian model with overlapping niches, and (III) a model emphasizing particulate, rather than continuous, ecological space. In Figure 5·9 we see one application of MacArthur's study. Model I, Gausian in prediction, predicts better than Models II and III the observed relative abundance of species. MacArthur's finding has now been demonstrated for other bird data, for snails (*Conus* sp.), for fossil mammals, and fossil as well as contemporary data on plant species abundance. This research is a major landmark in the elucidation of the ecological role of interspecific competition in the regulation of relative species abundance.

Another manifestation of the effects of ecological competition occurs at the level of intrapopulation variation. L. Van Valen has studied this variation in some bird species which are known to have broader ecological niches on islands in comparison to their counterparts on the European mainland. On the continent, these species have smaller niches or more specialized habitat requirements correlated with the occurrence of the birds in an avifauna possessing larger number of ecologically adjacent species. Van Valen finds that in the Canary Islands these species, abundant and ecologically wide-ranging, demonstrate greater coefficients of variations in bill size at the intrapopulational level than their respective populations on the mainland. The finding that populations of species are more variable in regions where their niches are wider is another manifestation of the role of interspecific ecological competition in the adaptation of organisms. Van Valen's study demonstrates again that competing species are negative density-dependent factors and thus elements of the natural selection operating on a given species (see Chapter 3).

Origin of Species-Specific Characters

Here we take up a problem still unresolved in evolution theory. It has to do with how, during phyletic evolution, a new character or adaptation arising by natural selection in one population of a species can spread throughout all populations of the species and thus become species-specific. What is the relative importance of intraspecific, interspecific, and environmental selection pressures in this process? This is the topic of the origin of new species adaptations. It is currently a major one in evolution theory, and we will consider it here as well as in Chapter 6 in a discussion of adaptive radiation.

INTRASPECIFIC VERSUS INTERSPECIFIC SELECTION PRESSURES

Can the presence or absence of a sympatric species represent an element of an isolate's biotic environment and thereby play a causal role in the adaptation of biological characters most efficient for that isolate? Theoretically, the answer is yes, and we need only examine relationships in the duck genus *Anas* to see possible examples. In this genus, members in allopatry or strong isolation tend to exhibit a lack of sexual dimorphism in contrast to their geographic, markedly dimorphic counterparts occurring in sympatry. However, here caution is necessary in drawing conclusions about the possibility of interspecific interactions. Geographic representatives of the genus *Anas* exhibiting a lack of, or decrease in, sexual dimorphism, such as certain members endemic to Pacific islands, are usually sedentary forms where the pair bond is maintained throughout the year. In contrast, the sympatric sexually dimorphic members are mostly migratory, and tend to break the pair bond immediately after the breeding season and to re-form pairs later. There thus appears to be strong intraspecific selection pressure for strengthening intersex communication and pair-bonding processes operating for sexual dimorphism in migratory species of *Anas*. In addition to this operation, interspecific selection pressures for sexual dimorphism as a means for avoidance of nonconspecific pairings (or reinforcement of auxiliary isolating mechanisms) may also play a role here. The relative importance of the two kinds of selection is unknown.

It is difficult to say that a species owes its specific characteristics to the presence, or former presence, of a related species. One can always argue that the differences were acquired in unknown ways during isolation or allopatry. The importance of interspecific selection pressures as factors influencing the development of species-specific characters would seem to become progressively greater as the sizes of the ranges of the pairs of competing or interacting isolates or related species become progressively smaller. There are two facets to this problem: (1) are most populations of both, or at least one, of the competing congeners in actual interspecific contact, and (2) are the ranges of both, or at least one, of these species relatively small? In the first case, genetic swamping would not operate against the results of interspecific selection pressures in at least one species. In the second case, both (or one) of the competing congeners would have, by virtue of restricted isolate size, a more favorable situation for reorganization of the gene pool in response to intraspecific, interspecific, and environmental selection pressures.

Finally, it should be clear that a variety of problems are encountered by species in sympatry, or living close to each other. Ecological ones have been described, but there are also behavioral ones. N. Tinbergen, M. Moynihan, and others have shown that there are adaptations to

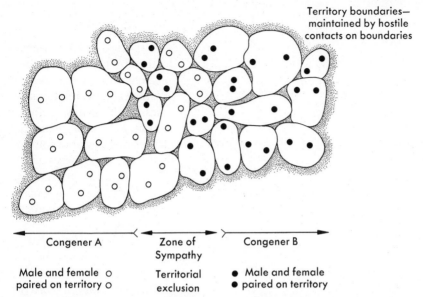

Territory boundaries—
maintained by hostile
contacts on boundaries

Congener A	Zone of Sympathy	Congener B
Male and female ○ paired on territory ○	Territorial exclusion	● Male and female ● paired on territory

Figure 5·10. Aspects of interspecific territoriality in birds. This usually occurs for pair-forming, territory-defending species in which males and females spend the majority of their feeding and other activities within a defended territory during the breeding season. For closely related species that are sympatric and quite similar to one another in species characters and recognition marks, hostility between individuals (particularly the males) of different as well as the same species effects a spatial separation of paired individuals of both species within a common habitat. Compare this figure with Figure 5·11.

avoid interspecific hostility. The relation of interspecific hostility to interspecific territorially is summarized in Figure 5·10, and, for the problem of competition between the sexes, in Figure 5·11.

Conclusion

Geographic or spatial isolation is a prerequisite for speciation in animal species. Isolates become incipient species which become races and these may become new species. The effect of geographic isolation is to retard or stop gene flow between the parental body of populations and that or those of the isolate. Absence of genetic swamping permits the new isolate to reorganize its gene pool and thus to differentiate in new genetic as well as biotic environments. Species occupy unique niches or ecological positions in the environment. No two species coexist in the same place in the same way at the same time. This is Gause's rule, and it stems from natural selection for avoidance of ecological competition between related species. Species do not usually exchange genes. This gap between species results from basic isolating mechanisms acquired in iso-

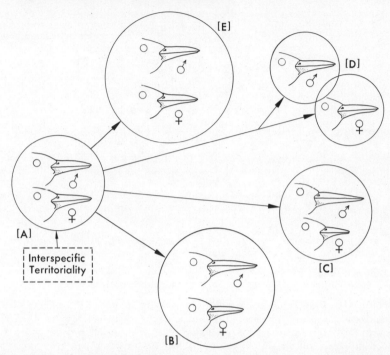

Figure 5·11. Alternate adaptations for reduction of intersexual competition in pair-forming, territory-defending birds. A: Continental species in which paired male and female individuals live together and defend (see Figure 5·10) a territory or environmental space throughout the year. **B:** Continental species which, related to the conditions of **A,** have increased dimorphism and increased size of the defended territory as a result of selection. **C:** Another course of adaptation whereby the sexes diverge in bill structure in association with differences in their respective niche utilization. **D:** Reduction of intersexual competition by selection for sexual differences in feeding territories. **E:** An immediate alternative to **A,** whereby the sexes remain morphologically and ecologically monomorphic, but exploit a larger feeding area or territory. These trends **(A–E)** are suggested by the findings of Selander, who has studied the adaptation of woodpeckers on continents and on islands. His findings, discussed in the text, suggest that on islands where competing species are absent and vacant ecological niches or habitats are available greater differences in differential niche utilization by the sexes may be manifested. It should be obvious to the student that this trend of adaptation **(C)** may also be demonstrated by a species on continents where competing species are absent and ecological niches are available. Compare this figure with Figure 6·10. [After R. K. Selander, *Condor,* 68: 113–151, 1966.]

lation and perfected or modified later by auxiliary devices as necessary in sympatry. A major unresolved problem is how new adaptations occur within a species, and spread throughout its distribution to become species-specific. It is easy to see how such phyletic evolution can occur in species on small islands or of small distributions on continents. For continentally distributed species, the problem is more complicated, with reduced isolation and increased gene flow retarding establishment and spread of new adaptations. Selection pressures operating for species differences are categorized as intraspecific, interspecific, or environmental. Except for species on small islands or with restricted distributions on continents, environmental and intraspecific selection pressures seem more important than interspecific ones in the origin of species-specific adaptations or characters.

Further Reading

Blair, W. F., Ed. *Vertebrate Speciation*. Austin: University of Texas Press, 1961.

Cain, S. A. *Foundations of Plant Geography*. New York: Harper and Brothers, 1944.

Dobzhansky, Th. *Genetics and the Origin of Species*. Third edition, second printing. New York: Columbia University Press, 1953.

Ehrlich, P. A., and R. W. Holm. *The Process of Evolution*. New York: McGraw-Hill Book Co., Inc., 1963.

Grant, V. *The Origin of Adaptations*. New York: Columbia University Press, 1963.

Huxley, J. *Evolution, the Modern Synthesis*. George Allen and Unwin, Ltd., 1942.

————, A. C. Hardy, and E. B. Ford, Eds. *Evolution as a Process*. London: George Allen and Unwin, Ltd., 1954.

Mayr, E. *Animal Species and Evolution*. Cambridge, Mass.: Harvard University Press, 1963.

————. "Isolation as an Evolutionary Factor." *Proceedings of the American Philosophical Society, 103:* 221–230, 1959.

————. *Systematics and the Origin of Species*. New York: Columbia University Press, 1942.

Schoener, T. W. "The Evolution of Bill Size Differences Among Sympatric Congeneric Species of Birds." *Evolution, 19:* 189–213, 1965.

Stebbins, G. L. *Variation and Evolution in Plants*. New York: Columbia University Press, 1950.

Van Valen, L. "Morphological Variation and Width of Ecological Niche." *American Naturalist, 99:* 377–390, 1965.

6

The Species as the Keystone
of Evolution

Each species is a biological experiment.

E. MAYR, 1963, p. 121.

IN PRECEDING CHAPTERS we have observed several times that evolutionists deduce mechanisms of evolution in two ways: one by the study of individual variations within populations; the other by comparison of group variations among populations, races, or species. In Chapter 5 a variety of group variations between populations and races was examined for evolutionary significance. These were intraspecific variations of a clinal or a discontinuous nature. We will now consider the origin of adaptive differences between species as well as the origin of new species or groups of organisms. The discussion presented will represent an analysis of adaptive radiation in relation to its role in the transspecific evolution of species.

Adaptive Differences Between Bird Species

The manifold aspects of adaptation were referred to in the preceding chapter, and it is self-evident that a comparison of adaptations among closely (and not so closely) related species may reveal the evolutionary significance of the adaptations studied. Also, D. Lack has pointed out that because of associated adaptations such comparisons are particularly revealing for differences between closely related species. The respective differences in biological characters between the ground-nesting gulls (*Larus* sp.) and the related cliff-nesting kittiwake (*Rissa tridoctyla*) demonstrate nicely the manifold effects of adaptation for one character on other associated or correlated characters of the organism. This is illustrated in Table 6·1. The study and its analysis rest upon the efforts and interpretations of E. Cullen and N. Tinbergen. A quick glance at Table 6·1 will show the large number of alterations that have occurred when a gull species becomes adapted to a new mode of life. Cullen and Tinbergen have studied the morphology, ecology, and behavior of the kittiwake compared to that of the gulls. Their findings reveal that the gulls are the ancestral type. New adaptations have been superimposed

TABLE 6·1

Adaptations for Ground Nesting in Gulls and for Cliff Nesting in the Kittiwake

GROUND-NESTING GULLS	KITTIWAKE
high predation-rate in nesting colonies	*predation pressure relaxed on cliffs*
1. Alarm-call frequent	1. Alarm-call rarer
2. Adults leave nest when predator some way distant	2. Remain on nest until predator very close
3. Vigorous attacks at predator intruding colony	3. Very weak attacks at most at intruding predator
4. Brooding birds disperse droppings and carry eggshells away from nest	4. Neither droppings nor eggshells dispersed
5. Young cryptic in appearance and behavior	5. Young not cryptic either in appearance or behavior
6. Clutch size normally three eggs	6. Clutch size normally two eggs
suited to life in colony on ground	*adapted to life on cliffs*
1. Several fighting methods Upright threat posture occurs Beak turned away in appeasement but not elaborately hidden	1. More specialized to fighting in one way (grabbing beak and twisting) No upright threat Beak turned away in appeasement and elaborately hidden
2. Young run away when attacked No neckband	2. Young do not run when attacked Possess black neckband
3. Copulation on the ground, female stands	3. Copulation on the tiny ledge or nest, female sits on tarsi
4. Nest material collected near nest, building not synchronized, individual collecting Nest-building technique relatively simple Mud not used	4. Nest material collected in unfamiliar places, synchronization of building and social collecting Nest-building technique more elaborate Mud as nest material
5. Young leave nest a few days after hatching Parents learn to recognize own young in a few days	5. Young have to stay on nest for long period Parents do not recognize own chicks at least up to the age of four weeks

Source: E. Cullen, *Ibis*, 99:275–302, 1957.

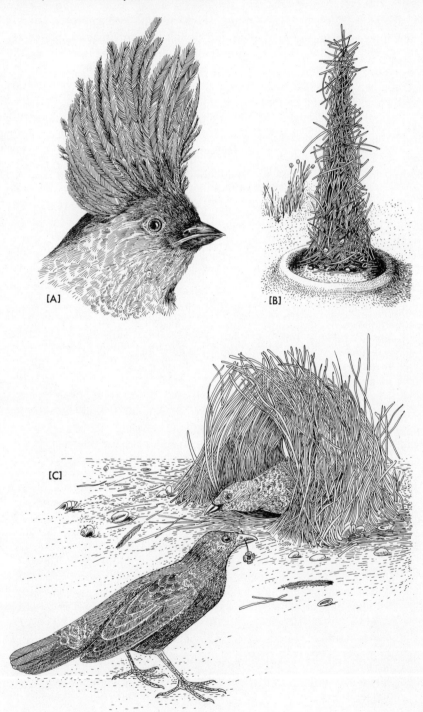

[A]

[B]

[C]

on older ones in the kittiwake during its adaptation and differentiation by selection in the cliff environment. When these results of adaptive radiation are peeled off, a core of older, more basic characters or adaptations remain. These are equivalent to those of ground-nesting gulls of the genus *Larus*.

In Figure 6·1 are shown examples of species differences and sexual specialization in the bowerbirds of Australia and the neighboring islands. The elaborate nature (plumage pattern and feather shapes) of the males in comparison to that of the females is most striking. This is an example of Darwin's principle of sexual selection. Darwin hypothesized a competition between males for females, with an intraspecific, intrasexual selection pressure favoring those male phenotypes (and their correlated genotypes!) more successful in attracting females. The two points of Darwin's sexual selection are competition for mates among males and selection by females of the more stimulating or attracting male phenotypes. Sexual selection as a form of intraspecific selection pressure is particularly important in polygamous species, species which do not form pair bonds, and species forming temporary pair bonds. There are good correlations (see Table 6·2) between sexual dimorphism and a seasonal pair bond on the one hand, and monomorphism and a permanent or animal pair bond on the other in bird groups such as the *Anatidae* (ducks, geese, swans) and the New World Warblers (*Parulidae*).

Examples of plumage dimorphism in birds are increasingly being found to be a compromise between various selection forces. These selection forces may be intraspecific (intrasexual and/or intersexual), interspecific, and environmental in operation. For example, inconspicuous females have been selected to achieve protective coloration (environmental selection) or for avoidance of intraspecific hostility in pair formation (intraspecific selection). Males may be brightly colored for attraction of females and repulsion in aggression of other males (intraspecific selection with intersexual and intrasexual elements) as well as for avoidance of hybridization or competition with other related species (interspecific selection). The unraveling of the kinds of selection pressures which operate for sexual dimorphism or monomorphism in birds as well as in other animal species is yet to be done. In Figure 6·2 exam-

Figure 6·1. Specialization in two species of the bowerbirds of Australia and New Guinea. These species do not form pairs. The males are promiscuous, and their specialized plumage patterns and behavioral activities (building of elaborate bowers to attract less specialized females) are consequences of natural selection, described as sexual selection by Darwin, involving attracting and copulating with as many females as possible. **A** and **B**: The male yellow-crested gardener (*Amblyornis macgregoriae*) and his bower. **C**: The satin bowerbird (*Ptilonorhynchus violaceus*) displaying to a female in his bower. [After A. J. Marshall, *The Bowerbirds*, Cambridge: The Cambridge University Press, 1955.]

TABLE 6·2

A Comparison of Plumage Dimorphism and Monomorphism with Sedentary and Migratory Habits for 105 Species of the American Wood Warblers (Parulidae)

	MONOMORPHIC (SEXES SIMILAR)	DIMORPHIC (SEXES DIFFERENT)
Migratory	27	23
Sedentary	53	2

$$\chi^2 = 23.65$$
$$p = 0.001 \text{ (highly significant)}$$

Source: T. H. Hamilton and R. H. Barth, Jr., *American Naturalist*, 96:129-144, 1962.

ples of tropical-to-temperate, monomorphic-to-dimorphic variation in species of the American wood warblers are shown. These trends are explained in terms of reproductive success achieved by reduced hostility

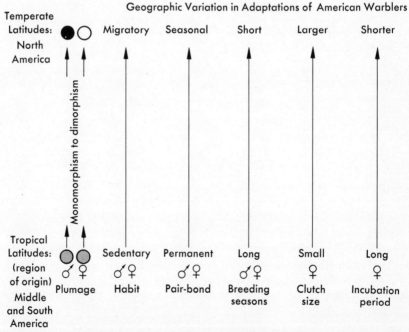

Figure 6·2. Examples of the tropical-to-temperate, monomorphic-to-dimorphic plumage trends in New World warblers (*Parulidae*). Although the birds themselves are not shown, the symbols denote a variety of characters (adaptations) that change when populations of species derived from the lower latitudes adapt to the unstable environments of North America.

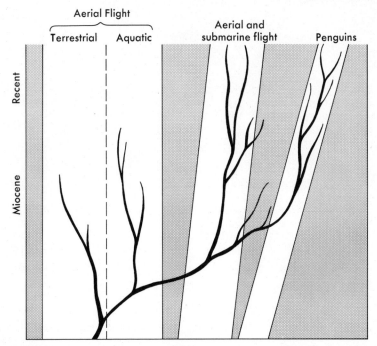

Figure 6·3. Diagram of penguin evolution. [From G. G. Simpson, *Major Features of Evolution*, New York: Columbia University Press, 1953.]

necessary for rapid breeding. Students should try to explain this example of monomorphism → dimorphism by the ideas already presented on adaptation.

Adaptive Radiation

Adaptive radiation may well be the major pattern of evolution. In a historical perspective, adaptive radiation is accelerated species formation with associated adaptive divergence. Paleontologists such as G. G. Simpson have adduced evidence that when a group of organisms enters a new adaptive zone previously unoccupied by the group, there may be rapid bursts of speciation and adaptive divergence into a variety of ecological niches. This assumes in general that there are (1) opportunities for speciation and (2) available or unoccupied ecological niches in the adaptive zone invaded by the group. In Figure 6·3, we see Simpson's visualization of such adaptive radiation for penguins. Note that there are three zones for penguins: aerial flight, aerial and submarine flight, and submarine flight. These zones were sequentially invaded by penguins in their evolution and they are now extinct in the aerial flight zone or subzone.

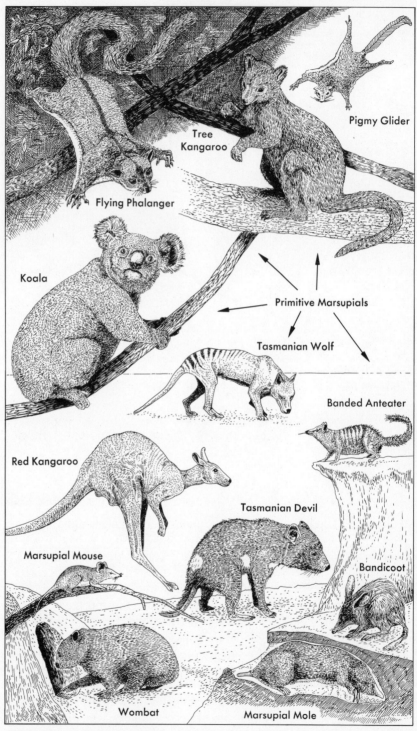

Pigmy Glider

Tree Kangaroo

Flying Phalanger

Koala

Primitive Marsupials

Tasmanian Wolf

Banded Anteater

Red Kangaroo

Tasmanian Devil

Marsupial Mouse

Bandicoot

Wombat

Marsupial Mole

Figure 6·4. Adaptive radiation of marsupials in Australia. [From a variety of sources.]

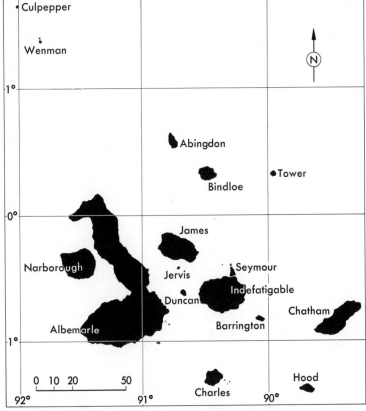

Figure 6·5. Map of the Galápagos Archipelago.

Perhaps because of the small size of the group (8,600 contemporary species) and their well-known taxonomy, birds provide some remarkably clear examples of adaptive radiation. The Galápagos finches (*Geospizinae*) and the Hawaiian honeycreepers (*Drepaniidae*) of isolated insular archipelagos are particularly instructive. We could cite many examples, and among these might be the cichlid fish species of the African-rift lake region and the marsupial mammals in Australia. Adaptive radiation of the latter group is illustrated by Figure 6·4.

David Lack's analysis of the adaptive radiation of the Galápagos or Darwin finches in the Galápagos Archipelago is a classical one, and it is only fitting that the last example of pattern in evolution for this book should deal with these bird species that gave Darwin his first insight into the mechanism of evolution. In Figure 6·5 we see a map of the islands of the archipelago. In general, the large islands are in the center of the archipelago, and are close to one another, while the smaller islands are both farther from one another and farther from the center of the archipelago. Various numbers of finch species occur in sympatry on the islands. The numbers of species and endemic subspecies are listed by island in Table 6·3. The species are illustrated in Figure 6·6, and we see that there are a variety of feeding types—for example, seed eaters, fruit eaters, cactus feeders, and insect eaters. Lack points out that the best explanation for this diverse assemblage of species is that from an original stock of colonizers reaching the archipelago, new forms have arisen by allopatric speciation. By dispersal, new species reach other islands and remain distinct. Since all of the Darwin finches are ecologically different by virtue of differences in habitat and/or feeding habits, Lack argues for ecological specialization occurring in isolation. Presumably further ecological specialization occurs in sympatry. We might say: the basic ecologic isolating mechanism of each species was acquired in allopatry and reinforced later as auxiliary adaptations perfected in sympatry.

In the context of speciation theory discussed in Chapter 5, let us now review the adaptive radiation of the Darwin finches. Isolation and va-

TABLE 6·3

The Distribution and Numbers of the Darwin Finches (Geospizinae) Within the Galápagos Archipelago

ISLAND	NUMBER OF SPECIES	NUMBER OF SPECIES OCCURRING AS ENDEMICS
Culpepper	4	2
Wenman	5	1
Abingdon	9	2
Bindloe	7	1
Narborough	9	0
Albemarle	10	1
Tower	4	3
Hood	3	2
Chatham	7	3
Charles	9	2
Jervis	9	0
James	10	0
Barrington	7	1
Duncan	9	0
Indefatigable	10	0
Seymour	8	0

Source: T. H. Hamilton and I. Rubinoff, *Evolution*, 17:383–403, 1963.

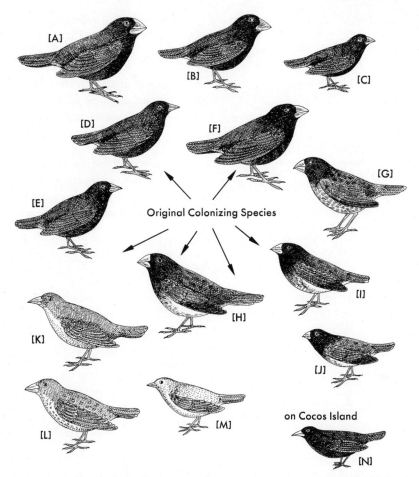

Figure 6·6. The Darwin finches. A: *Geospiza magnirostris.* **B:** *G. fortis.* **C:** *G. fuliginosa.* **D:** *G. difficilis.* **E:** *G. scandens.* **F:** *G. conirostus.* **G:** *Camanhynchus crassirostris.* **H:** *C. psittacula.* **I:** *C. pauper.* **J:** *C. parvulus.* **K:** *C. pallidus.* **L:** *C. heliobates.* **M:** *Certhidea olivacea.* **N:** *Pinaroloxias inornata* (of Cocos Island). [After D. Lack.]

cant ecological niches are necessary for adaptive radiation. These conditions were met by the original, colonizing population of finches. All islands were soon inhabited, and race formation to a certain degree occurred. But in the inner core of islands, where isolation is reduced, interisland dispersal and genetic swamping would retard population divergence and the formation of new races. In fact, if one compares the data on Table 6·3 with Figure 6·7, it is seen that endemic races or peculiar forms are more frequent on the outer than the inner islands. Thus we may assume that new races arise more frequently on the outer

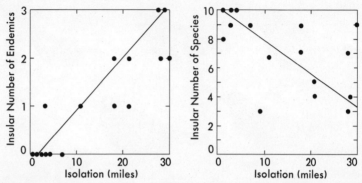

Figure 6·7. Correlation between isolation (distance from nearest neighboring island) and insular number of endemic subspecies of Darwin finches. A: Positive correlation. **B:** Negative correlation. The figure shows the greater frequencies of endemics on isolated islands and the greater number of species, but fewer endemics, on the nonisolated islands comprising the archipelago's core. [Data from T. H. Hamilton and I. Rubinoff, *Evolution 17:* 388–403, 1963.]

islands where isolation prevents gene flow and thus promotes endemic differentiation or race formation (see Figure 6·7). It is believed that new forms originate on the more isolated islands and then disperse back to the central islands of the archipelago. In these islands, larger land areas and greater habitat diversity would permit high degrees of sympatry. In this way we can envision an adaptive radiation cycle for the Darwin finches in the manner shown in Figure 6·8. This has species arising on outer islands, dispersing to inner islands, diverging *further* there in their ecological characteristics, dispersing eventually back to the outer islands, and so on. The problem of extinction of species in the cycle is ignored here, but in Figure 6·9 we can see W. L. Brown, Jr.'s interpretation of adaptive radiation and extinction of honeycreepers in the Hawaiian Islands.

Individual Versus Group Selection

Every contemporary species is the result of adaptive radiation. But only in the case of the relatively rapid speciation and adaptation of the members of a monophyletic group do we see the process as described

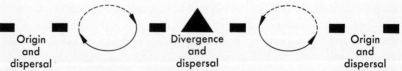

Figure 6·8. A hypothetical cycle for the adaptive radiation of the Darwin finch species in the Galápagos Archipelago. For explanation, see text. [After T. H. Hamilton and I. Rubinoff, *Evolution, 17:* 388–403, 1963.]

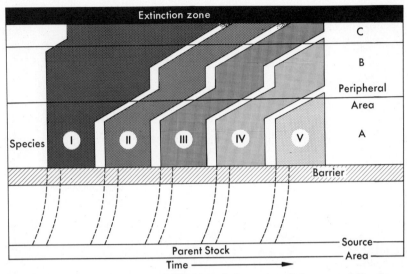

Figure 6·9. W. L. Brown's visualization of the axis origin → specialization → extinction for adaptive radiation as exemplified by the Hawaiian honeycreeper (*Drepaniidae*). [From W. L. Brown, Jr., *Systematic Zoology*, 7: 157–168.]

above for the Darwin finches or the marsupials in Australia (see Figure 6·4). The basis of such adaptive radiation—ignoring for the moment the prerequisite of allopatric speciation—is selection for avoidance of ecological competition by the individuals which comprise the competing populations involved. In this context, adaptive radiation can be expected at the intraspecific level as well as the interspecific one described above. If the individual is the unit of selection, then in pair-forming animals alleviation of intersexual competition may be a factor contributing to adaptive divergence in certain ecological situations. R. K. Selander thus explains the phenomenon of increased size dimorphism for certain woodpecker species which occur on islands in the West Indies (Figure 6·10). He finds that on islands where only one species of woodpecker occurs, that species exhibits a pronounced sexual dimorphism (males larger than females) in bill and body size, as well as a greater abundance in comparison to related species occurring in sympatry on other islands or on the American mainland. Selander finds that the two sexes of the more dimorphic species have feeding positions and frequencies more different from each other than those of the sexes of the less dimorphic species that occur in sympatry. He suggests that at the intraspecific level, adaptive radiation of the two sexes has occurred. Absence of interspecific competition and differential niche utilization are the key aspects of this radiation. In this example, we see again the negative density-dependent nature of individuals in the opera-

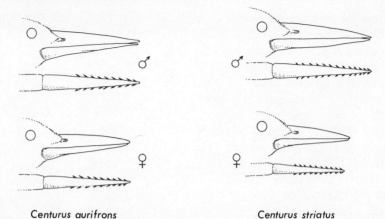

Centurus aurifrons   Centurus striatus

Figure 6·10. Sexual dimorphism in the head, bill, and tongue structure for an insular species of woodpecker (*Centurus striatus*) and a continental species (*Centurus aurifrons*). For explanation, see text and Figure 5·10. [After R. K. Selander, *Condor, 68:* 113–151, 1966.]

tion of natural selection on other individuals (for intersexual-intra-specific situations as well as interspecific ones!). Furthermore, we see also that the interpretation given demands that the *individual* be considered the unit of natural selection.

Adaptive radiation of animal species results from repeated allopatric speciation in regions with empty ecological niches. In this way new adaptations are favored, and older ones marked or modified at various rates of change. In the preceding chapter the problem of the origin and spread within species of new adaptations was introduced. At least for species of small islands or restricted continental distribution it is not difficult to see how new adaptations arise and become species-specific. (By species-specific character is meant one which is possessed by every individual of the species.) But how does this occur during phyletic evolution of species whose populations are widely distributed on continents? Evolutionists now think of two ways whereby this might occur: one is by spread to adjacent populations of individuals (whose genotypes' phenotypes are the characters we designate above) having increased fitness over other individuals; the other way involves spread of one population at the expense of another. This latter is known as group selection. Most evolutionists now favor the former hypothesis. But the problem of the degree of importance in evolution of interdeme selection and/or interindividual selection is a timely and critical one. Part of the problem centers around the fact that while comparisons of fitness (W) for reproducing genotypes or individuals *within* a population can be made, it is difficult to compare fitness $(\overline{W})$ *between* demes or populations. (By *fitness* of an individual is meant the proportionate contribution of its offspring and thus genotype to the next generation, and it is necessary to remember that proportionate contributions means in comparison to the contributions of offspring made by other individuals.) Fitness is sometimes called *adaptive value* or *selective value* (Chapters 3 and 4). In practice, the relative fitness of two individuals is compared, with the individual or genotype contributing the larger number of offspring to the next generation being assigned a fitness of 1. The other genotype will have a fitness of $1 - x$. So the fitness of the former individual is $W = 1/(1 - x)$, that is, the ratio of the offspring contributed by the two individuals to the next generation (refer back to Chapters 3 and 4). The *average fitness* of a population then would be $\overline{W}$, the mean of the summation of the W values of all individuals. For discussions and explanations of the concepts of individual and population fitness (W and $\overline{W}$), students are referred to texts on population genetics, the paper by R. C. Lewontin cited at the end of Chapter 3, and the book of G. C. Williams cited at the end of this chapter.

Recently Williams has given a critique of the relative importance of *individual selection* and *group selection* in adaptation and evolution. The concept of individual selection (between-individual or interindividual selection) is Darwinian in the sense that selection operates on individuals for selection of one allele or another possessed by one individual or another. The concept of group selection, sometimes referred to as between-group, interpopulation, or interdeme selection, refers to natural selection of groups of individuals. The latter type of selection is thought to give rise to the so-called biotic adaptations. (For a discussion of this topic and a defense of group selection, students are referred to Wynne-Edwards' book cited at the end of this Chapter. For a rebuttal of Wynne-Edwards' thesis, see Lack's 1966 book.) Group selection has also been resorted to by various authors to explain situations wherein it *appears* that the interests of the individual have been altruistically subordinated or curtailed for the interest or advantage of the group as a whole. Examples here are colonial insects with their caste systems and members which do not reproduce, and the more well-known instances of social adaptation. Williams points out that individual selection is sufficient in nearly all cases to explain adaptations previously thought to be a result of group selection. Here it is useful to remember (see Chapter 3) that other individuals are part of an individual's environment, and thus, as discussed in Chapter 5, are part of the negative density-dependent situation in the operation of natural selection on that individual. An individual living in close proximity to many other individuals may well achieve higher fitness if his or her genotype is one for cooperation, for small clutch size, for shorter lifespan, for delayed breeding, or some other specialized activity. The idea here is that in such special social or ecological situations, the offspring of that individual will carry the parent's genotype into future generations in greater frequencies. This is no more than Darwinian individual selection, and Williams concludes that most social adaptations or group actions should be considered a statistical summation of the results of individual selection, and not a result of group selection. In the case of social insects (for example, honeybees) with some individuals being sterile, it appears best to consider these individuals not self-sacrificing, but merely phenotypic extensions or fingertips of the queen bee's genotype. It is along these lines that we have emphasized throughout this book that the *reproducing individual* is the primary unit of natural selection.

We will not consider the problem further, but students should recognize the relation of interdeme selection to the Darwin-Wallace concept of evolution by natural selection—which considers the individual to be the unit of selection.

The Species as the Major Unit of Evolution

In this book we have seen that mutation, recombination, selection, and isolation are, by Mayr's expression, the four cornerstones of evolution. We have observed that natural selection results in differential reproduction, and thus adapts populations. The results of adaptation in turn reflect evolutionary change. The phenotype of an organism is considered a compromise between various, sometimes conflicting, selection forces. The reproducing individual is here taken as the unit of natural selection and gene substitution as the unit process in (population) adaptation. These factors, working on a background of genetic variations, result in the adaptive divergence of populations. Thus they work for new genetic equilibria for gene pools. But speciation is responsible for the gaps between species and thus the origin of discontinuities—which in turn make possible evolutionary advances. In this context, it becomes clear that the species is the major unit of evolution. For,

The evolutionary significance of species is now quite clear. Although the evolutionist may speak of broad phenomena, such as trends, adaptations, specializations, and regressions, they are really not separable from the progression of entities that display these trends, the species. The species are the real units of evolution, as the temporary incarnation of harmonious, well-integrated gene complexes. And speciation, the production of new gene complexes capable of ecological shifts, is the method by which evolution advances. Without speciation there would be no diversification of the organic world, no adaptive radiation, and very little evolutionary progress. The species, then, is the keystone of evolution.

E. MAYR, 1963, p. 621.

Further Reading

Dobzhansky, Th. *Genetics and the Origin of Species.* Third edition, revised. New York: Columbia University Press, 1953.

Grant, V. *The Origin of Adaptations.* New York: Columbia University Press, 1963.

Hamilton, T. H., and Ira Rubinoff. "Isolation, Endemism, and Multiplication of Species in the Darwin Finches." *Evolution, 17:* 388–403, 1963.

Lack, D. *Darwin's Finches.* Cambridge, England: Cambridge University Press, 1947.

———. "Evolutionary Ecology." *Journal of Animal Ecology, 34:* 223–231, 1965.

———. *Population Studies of Birds.* Oxford, England: Oxford University Press, 1966.

Mayr, E. *Animal Species and Evolution.* Cambridge, Mass.: Harvard University Press, 1963.

Rensch, B. *Evolution Above the Species Level.* New York: Columbia University Press, 1960.

Selander, R. K. "Sexual Dimorphism and Differential Niche Utilization in Birds." *Condor, 68:* 113–151, 1966.

Simpson, G. G. *The Major Features of Evolution.* Third printing. New York: Columbia University Press, 1961.

Stebbins, G. L., Jr. *Variation and Evolution in Plants.* New York: Columbia University Press, 1951.

Tinbergen, N. "Comparative Studies of the Behaviour of Gulls (Laridae): A Progress Report." *Behavior, 15:* 1–70, 1959.

Williams, G. C. *Adaptation and Natural Selection.* New Jersey: Princeton University Press, 1966.

Wynne-Edwards, V. C. *Animal Dispersion in Relation to Social Behaviour.* London: Oliver and Boyd, 1962.

Index

Page numbers in **boldface** refer to illustrations and tables.